SIMEON'S SWORD
MARY REMEMBERS

by Alice E. W. Smith

BARBEDWIRE
PUBLISHING
LAS CRUCES, NEW MEXICO

Published by Barbed Wire Publishing
270 Avenida de Mesilla
Las Cruces, New Mexico 88005 USA

The fonts used in this book are Galahad and Kinesis MM
Book and cover design by Vicki Ligon

First printing: October 2002.
Printed in the United States of America.

ISBN #0-9711930-9-6

1   2   3   4   5

This book is written in memory
of the mothers in Bethlehem whose babies died
when the Holy Family fled to Egypt.

It is dedicated to my four sons,
Terry, David, William, and Timothy,
who are the joy of my life

to my daughters-in-law,
Mary, Joni, and Sue,
whom I love as daughters and friends

and to my grandchildren,
Tara, Harold, Nathaniel, Noah, Hannah, and Samantha,
who are indescribably wonderful!

SIMEON'S SWORD

Table of Contents

Acknowledgements

Thank you to Karla, for all your typing.

Thank you to my husband, Terry Sr.,
for always supporting me in my wild dreams.

Introduction

I began this book in an attempt to share the life of Mary the mother of Jesus, because I believe she can teach us a great deal about what our lives ought to be. Life became very difficult for Mary when she agreed to serve God with her entire being. Old Simeon, in the temple, at the baby Jesus' dedication, warned Mary, "and a sword will pierce your soul, too." I believe she felt Simeon's sword, not once, but many times. Yet Mary remained faithful through all the hardships, even though she was human like you and me. She is a model of faith for us all.

I learned from the late Reverend Doctor Bruce Edward Schein that an understanding of the culture, geography, and customs of Bible times is essential to an understanding of our Lord, his teachings, and the Bible stories themselves. Each story is, in fact, infused with meaning so deep that there is always more to learn. For example, consider the Christmas story. Having learned that the shepherds were outcasts—considered ungodly thieves and that the magi were, in fact, magicians—hated by Jew and Roman alike—is the story saying that Jesus came to the down trodden, the rejected, the hated, those judged by others, and that we, too, must care about such? Is it saying that the hearts and minds of "religious" people like ourselves may become so full of our own holiness that there is no room for God to be born within us, and that we must be cautious, lest we become those who are so caught up in feelings of self-righteousness that we fail to hear the angels sing? There are so many questions that each of us must ask ourselves, seeking the guidance of the Holy Spirit, and finding the meaning of the stories for our own lives. But we can only truly ask the questions when we have certain knowledge that in Jesus' day could go unspoken, because it was so common, but in our day is not known. Since I learn best from novels, I began to weave into the story of Mary's life such information in an attempt to portray the story more nearly as it actually happened

—not as we have softened and westernized it to be. My hope is that some of the original meaning will come to light, and the depth of the story will be revealed.

Most of my information comes from Pastor Schein, who was a professor at Trinity Lutheran Seminary in Columbus, Ohio. He was a unique scholar. He had served as a pastor, earned a doctorate in the gospel of John, studied at a Jewish seminary, moved to the Holy Land where he worked for Lutheran World Federation, served a congregation, led people on pilgrimages, talked religion with Arab sheiks, argued with rabbis, and became one of only three people in the world who could walk the Holy Land, telling the stories as he went. History is piled upon history in that small land, and it was an ancient custom that the stories be told as people traveled. Wherever he went, Pastor Schein always wore a clergy collar to identify himself as a slave of Christ, like Mary, whom he regarded as a woman of great faith.

In my research, I have also consulted the *Midrash Rabbah*, (Soncino Press, 1983) and the *Mishnah* (Oxford University Press, 1983) both of which contain extra-Biblical teachings which Jesus would have known and accepted, *Pontius Pilate*, by Paul Maier (Doubleday, 1968), a source of history, and *The Torah, A Modern Commentary* (Union of American Hebrew Congregations, 1981). Other references consulted were numerous and are not listed here.

Mary is not mentioned often in the Bible, so I have skipped periods of time in some parts of the story, and in others parts I have filled in using my imagination in order to get Mary to the right place at the right time. I have noted fictional characters for the sake of clarity and have used footnotes to offer explanations when it seemed appropriate, needed, or of interest. When I began writing, it was my intent to use non-sexist language. However, even though God is neither male nor female, I cannot bring myself to refer to God as "It." The repetitious use of the word "God" in order to avoid a pronoun became very cumbersome and, I felt, distracted from the narrative. Therefore, I have reluctantly reverted to the generic "He." I hope that sometime in the near future a new pronoun will be coined for the English language which will eliminate the dilemma of wondering how to refer to God. I tell the story in the first person, because I tried to become Mary as I reflected and wrote. It is a story I tell in hopes of honoring the Holy Mother, and it is a story I tell because we have much to learn from her life about trusting God to see us through the hard times, and about following even when it means it will make life more difficult.

Mary is, indeed, a model of faith for us all. So, now, I am Mary and this is my story.

CHAPTER 1

The Annunciation

On my way back from the well, I caught a glimpse of Joseph working in his carpentry shop. He was absorbed with making a threshing sled for a farmer and was completely unaware of my presence. I saw the muscles ripple in his arms and the sweat trickle down his strong handsome face. The sight of him warmed me! Wanting to be alone so I could dream of him and enjoy the waves of emotion that fanned through my body, I hurried home. Lowering my jar of water to the ground near the front door, I went around to the side of the house where there was shade. I sat down on the dry rocky ground next to a bench and rested my back against the cool stone of the building, setting my mind free to think thoughts of Joseph and the day when we would wed.

Since my family's move from Sephoris to Nazareth, I had seen Joseph often when I went to the well to fetch water.[1] He was several years older than I,[2] so even when I was quite small, Joseph was there, working, making farm implements[3] to be used in the rich valley below. When I was running and playing with other children, Joseph would sometimes stop his work and talk with us. He was a kind man, who always wore a gentle smile, and even as a child, I had loved him.

Not long ago, I was betrothed to Joseph. We exchanged vows, a

---

1. Girls were responsible for carrying enough water from the well to the home to meet all the family's needs each day. This occupied most of their daylight hours.

2. According to tradition, Joseph was older than Mary, perhaps even married a couple of times before, and died during Jesus' teen years. The fact that we do not hear of Joseph after the trip to the temple when Jesus was twelve fits with this tradition.

3. The Greek word translated carpenter means artisan, which could be either a stone mason or a carpenter. Since wood was scarce, stone was used for most items, i.e. houses, tables, chairs, etc., such items being made by stone masons. Carpenters, on the other hand, made farm implements—sickle and hoe handles, threshing sleds, etc. They also fashioned items such as crutches when needed, but their main products were agricultural. Since Jesus so often used agricultural examples in his teaching, we have traditionally assumed that he was one who dealt with agricultural implements and would consequently have a good working knowledge of what farming was about. Therefore, we have called him a carpenter.

contract was made, legally binding us to one another, and soon Joseph and I would begin a year of living together in a non-sexual relationship, in the presence of relatives. Joseph would try my cooking, and I would see what he was like when I burned the bread. We would look at one another across the breakfast table and experience the best and the worst that each had to offer. Joseph would continue his work in the shop attached to his home, but we would take our meals at the same table, sleep in the same house, and be together for the Sabbath when no one worked. Then, at the end of the year, we would decide whether we should continue our relationship by entering into marriage or end the betrothal by divorce.

There was no doubt in my mind that the wedding would take place. On that day, Joseph would go to his home, make preparations, and then come for me with all his friends, bringing the bride price that he and my father had agreed upon earlier. When Joseph arrived, I would be wearing an elaborately embroidered dress that I would prepare during the year of betrothal, and my dowry[4] would be draped across my forehead. After Joseph paid my father, there would be a procession. Joseph would ride a white donkey and I would walk behind him. Our friends would surround us, cheering us on, as we walked to Joseph's house where the wedding canopy awaited us. There the marriage would be consummated[5] and we would feast and celebrate for a week!

Soon after that, hopefully, God would bless me, and I would give Joseph a child. My body filled with joy at the thought of a husband and a baby of my own to tend. I closed my eyes and the pleasure engulfed me, leaving me completely unprepared for the sound of a strange man's voice.

"Hello, favored one!" he said.

Startled, I jerked my head up quickly, my eyes wide with fright.

A man[6] stood very near, looking down at me! Why was he talking to me?[7] "Favored one?" Was he flirting?

What kind of a woman did he think I was!? Now indignant as well

---

4. A dowry consisted of coins given to a woman by her parents and worn as a headband on her forehead on her wedding day and after her marriage. The coins were not only a sign of worth, but more importantly a kind of life insurance policy, to be used in the event something tragic happened to her husband. Women had few options in providing for themselves, so the dowry was important.

5. The sexual act constituted the wedding. See Chapter 9 pages 77–79 for more details.

6. Angels who brought messages were indistinguishable from men, e.g. the angels who came to tell Abraham that Sarah would soon become pregnant. Genesis 18:2.

7. Men talked only with women of their immediate households and only within the privacy of their own homes.

as frightened, I was inching my back up the wall, rising toward a standing position. Once on my feet, I would make a dash for the front door. Recognizing my intentions, the stranger cried urgently, "God is with you!"

I stared at him, puzzled by this greeting. Normally, it was, "The Lord be with you!" and the reply would be, "And also with you!" But this man had said, "God *is* with you!" like a statement of fact. He said it with such authority that I felt compelled to listen, but only for a moment!

I was now standing and edging my way toward the front corner of the house. Seeing what I was doing, he implored, "Don't be afraid!" Then, as if to establish his position, he cried, "You have found favor with God."

Uncertain whether to scream or to listen, I stopped and stared at the stranger. Such puzzling things he kept saying! It didn't appear that he meant me harm, and there was something about him that inspired trust. I listened as he continued.

"You are going to become pregnant and have a son."

A wave of fear swept over me again. Was he going to rape me? I wanted to run, but my muscles seemed paralyzed.

"You are to name him Jesus, which means, 'God saves,'" he continued. I felt completely confused. Somehow, I trusted this man without knowing why. Were Joseph and I to have a son and name him Jesus? Thoughts raced through my mind. If we had a baby, I would exercise my prerogative as a woman and name it myself, choosing a name that said something about the child. My mother had named me Mary—plump or chubby one[8]!

"God saves." I pondered the meaning. Was I to have a son that would be a religious leader, perhaps? Why was I inclined to believe this man? Why was I standing here with him, listening? Was he a prophet?

"He will be called God's son!" the man continued.

God's son? All our kings had been called "God's son!" Was my son to be a king? That hardly seemed likely!

"God will put him on David's throne, but unlike David's, your son's kingdom will have no end. It will last forever."

A king like David whose kingdom will have no end! Was this baby

---

8. Mary or Miriam means chubby, and in a land where food is scarce, being "chubby" is something to be desired.

to be the Messiah? Could it be? Was I to be the mother of the Christ? A sense of unreality gripped me. My mind continued to race, analyzing what this stranger was saying. The Messiah, the Christ, literally "the anointed one," would be a person of God's own choosing. David had been an anointed one, and many of our people looked for a king like David to come as the Messiah. David—warrior, politician, man of deep faith, richly blessed by God! Not that David was perfect. Some of his sins were atrocious! But, invariably, once he realized that he had done wrong, it grieved him. Filled with repentance, he would then turn to God. "Take not your Holy Spirit from me!" he had prayed on one occasion, so grievous was his sin. Then, reassured of the steadfast love and forgiveness of God, David quickly moved on—charging ahead, living life to the fullest, secure in the knowledge that God would always be waiting, arms open wide, to welcome David back when he recognized his own sinfulness. Through this sure confidence in God's forgiveness, David was set free to accomplish great things. And God loved David dearly, as we also love those who accept our gifts with confidence and joy. So it was that David was a good king, and God's people longed for another like David; someone who possessed military and political genius, who would come and deliver us from the enemies that kept us in bondage and prevented us from being free.

Yet not everyone believed that the Messiah would be another David, or that he would come as a baby among us. Some believed that Elijah would be the Christ, that since he did not die, but was taken into heaven by God instead, he would be the one to return to save God's people. Elijah would come, not with military and political skills, but with deep faith and miraculous powers, and he would make us free!

Still others looked for the prophet Moses[9] to return. He had delivered the people from slavery and fed them with bread from heaven. If Moses returned, we would not only be free, but be fed as well!

Others looked for one like Solomon or Aaron, but however the Messiah came, it would be a wondrous thing! Each time a baby boy was born, there was the unspoken hope that this was the one, the Messiah who would free all God's people, and who would establish God's kingdom once and for all time!

But a strange man stood before me, and I struggled to focus my mind on what was happening. Why was I standing beside the house with

9. When the Bible refers to *the* prophet, it refers to Moses, e.g. John 1:21.

a stranger instead of running inside for safety? Was it because he had mentioned a king like David? Joseph and I were both descendants of David!

I was beginning to trust this man—or was he a man? Sarah's story kept popping into my head. Angels had appeared to her husband, Abraham, when God drew near with the message that Sarah would bear a son, Isaac. Could this be an angel? I was overwhelmed with trying to understand this man, or angel, or whatever he was. At the same time though, a sense of peace had stolen over me, and then I felt a warmth filling me, a warmth stronger than I knew when dreaming of Joseph. Joseph!! Was this to be Joseph's baby—or not? Maybe not?! With that thought, I lost all sense of security, and all questions about royalty, kingdoms and angels vanished from my head, and I blurted out, "How can this be? I'm a virgin!"

I felt my face flush, but the man was undaunted. He answered calmly, "The power of God will cover you!"

Then it was not to be Joseph's baby! My mind raced. God's son? Not born of the will of a man, but of God's will?

He continued, "Your child will be set apart for God and will be called the Son of God."

All my thinking ceased. I just stared at this creature who stood before me, unsure even yet of what he was.

Then, as if wanting to help me overcome my doubts and confusion, he revealed information that I could verify. "Your elderly barren relative, Elizabeth, is pregnant—six months now. You see, nothing is impossible with God."

"All right," I said. "Let it be as you say." Long ago, in the beginning of time, God had spoken those words, "Let there be ...," and whatever he named came into being. I reflected his words, believing that if God could create the universe, he could create a pregnancy within me. Then I added, "I am God's slave."[10]

The peace that settled over me and continued to grow in spite of the strange things that were happening, was reassurance that this messenger was from God.

Suddenly the man vanished, and I knew with all certainty that an angel had visited me. I had been in God's presence!

---

10. The word commonly translated, servant, here is actually the Greek word *doulas*, meaning slave, which has a different connotation—ownership as opposed to employment.

As I lay in bed that night, I thought about what had happened during the day. Could it be true, was I to give birth to the Messiah? It was a frightening thought! Could I mother the Messiah and do a good job? Surely, it was not true! After all, I was from Nazareth, the poor section of northern Palestine. The village lay on top of a rocky hill high above the plains and the coast below. The trade routes with all the caravans carrying goods of wealth from one country to another were not far from us. We could see the wheat fields that made their owners wealthy, and the lush vineyards that produced the finest wine in the world, but none of it was ours. Nazareth was not far from Sephoris, that strong, wealthy, Jewish center of activity where I had begun my life. In Nazareth, we were familiar with wealth, but ours was a poor village atop a poor rocky hill. Some would joke, "Could anything good come out of Nazareth?" The Messiah from Nazareth? I wondered—and I his mother? I, a poor young woman, not of royalty, not betrothed to a priest, but to a carpenter? And Joseph? Where did he fit in? We were to be married, and I loved him. Finally, sleep came.

CHAPTER 2

The Visit to Elizabeth

After I finally drifted off that night, I slept soundly. When I awakened, it was to the impatient sound of my mother's voice calling my name. I opened my eyes reluctantly to find sunlight streaming in the window. Obviously, I had overslept. My mother was talking as I sat up and struggled to awaken myself. As I pushed hair away from my forehead and ran my fingers through it, Mother was saying something about some strange news that she had heard and wanted to tell me. I slowly got up off my mat on the floor, feeling unusually tired and a little nauseous. The previous day's events had abandoned my mind completely. I dressed and joined my mother, and when she began to share the latest talk with me, glimpses of those startling happenings began to come back. "I made a trip to the well this morning since you weren't up," she said a bit accusingly. "Everyone was talking about Isaac's[1] family and what they heard in Jerusalem." A chill crept through me, as I remembered the man behind the house. Talk about strange news! I wondered what Mother would think if I told her what had happened to me yesterday. She would no doubt accuse me of some foolish, girlish daydreaming. But, maybe it was a dream! I fell captive to my own thoughts, hoping it was not true. It was frightening, but it seemed so real!

Mother continued talking while I was thinking. Hearing the name Elizabeth brought me back to what she was saying. "Elizabeth and Zachariah were in Jerusalem so Zachariah could serve his time in the Holy of Holies. Being selected to serve is quite an honor. Once a year, one priest enters that inner sanctum, and all sorts of arrangements have to be made. The selection is done by lot, so it is actually God who chooses which priest it will be. Would you believe—she eyed me as if the next bit of information should shock me. "They even had a woman lined up for

1. Fictitious character.

Zachariah to marry in case something happened to Elizabeth. You know only married priests are allowed to go into the Holy of Holies. I wonder how Elizabeth felt about having her replacement ready!" she laughed.

"I wonder how Elizabeth would feel about being pregnant in her old age," I mumbled to myself. Had my mother told me that her old cousin was with child, instead of prattling on about nothing, I would have been more interested. Until I sorted out this angel business, she could tell me that the Temple itself had fallen down, and I would not care. Mother was still talking. I worked to pull myself away from my own thoughts, so I could hear what she was saying.

"...completed the ritual cleansing of Zachariah. Then they put those fancy clothes on him, and he went into the forbidden room according to the custom. I think that would really be scary, don't you?"

Mother was relishing every bit of this story, and I was growing impatient. What would really be scary was if old Elizabeth were pregnant. "You don't know what scary is," I muttered, not intending her to hear.

"What did you say? Will you wake up and stop mumbling?!" she said. "Anyway, that's not the scariest part." She looked at me curiously as though she sensed something was different, but she was too caught up in her story to let anything interrupt. "Zachariah was in there a long time, and people began to wonder if something was wrong.[2] Maybe he had seen God or Satan and was lying on the floor dead or needing help. They were trying to decide who should go in after him, but no one wanted to risk going in without doing it according to the law. Who knows what would happen to them if they did."

"They might get pregnant," I thought dryly, "and not know if it was a dream or if it really happened."

"Anyway, while they were trying to decide, old Zachariah came out on his own, much to everyone's relief."

"Is this what she got me up to tell me?" I wondered. Then I felt a little guilty for not being more attentive. After all, Elizabeth was a relative,

---

2. There was a superstitious belief in biblical times that Satan—the Accuser, who always points out our faults to God (e.g. in Job), was in the Holy of Holies with God. So the priest would light the incense before going into that inner sanctum, not only to keep from seeing God (which would result in death), but also to protect himself from Satan. Once inside, he would perform the rituals and get out as quickly as possible, so as not to worry those who waited for him outside. The Pharisees insisted that people stop believing such things and that the priest wait until he was inside to light the incense. These fears were alive in Zachariah's time. Hence, the people worried about Zachariah.

and Zachariah had been honored. Mother loved to hear and repeat news from outside Nazareth. So did I! I tried to be more alert, but there was a queasiness in my stomach, and I felt so tired.

"But the relief didn't last long," she said. "When he came out, he started making signs with his hands. The people thought the old man had gone crazy or was possessed. Then they realized that he couldn't talk at all! Something had happened to him in the Holy of Holies!" She had my attention at last, and she knew it. She went on with even more enthusiasm. "The people all decided that he had seen a vision of an angel!"

"Angel?" I thought. "I wish someone could describe one for me." I continued listening to my mother.

"Anyway, they let him finish his time of service, even though he didn't regain his voice. When he had completed his time, he and Elizabeth went home. And you'll never believe the next part!" She paused, enjoying every minute of having my complete attention. I was wide awake now. My breathing had ceased, and I stared at my mother, my mouth hanging open. Would she ever go on and finish the story? Mother was beginning to stare back at me, and, as I became conscious of how I looked, I tried to compose myself. Studying me with uncertainty, she continued. "Now, it seems that old Elizabeth is pregnant—six months along already! What do you think of that?" she asked. What did I think?! I felt as if I had just been hit by a Roman chariot going at full horsepower, and Mother wanted to know what I was thinking! When I heard the news about Elizabeth, all the previous day's events came rushing back at once. I had tried to put them out of my mind, hoping that I had dreamed them. I was willing to do anything but deal with the reality of God's demands on my life. The sound of my mother's voice became faint as my mind raced. Dear God, it must be true! The angel had told me that Elizabeth was pregnant. As I struggled, trying to deal with what I had hoped was only a dream, my mother's voice slowly grew louder, and I realized that she was no longer telling a story about Elizabeth and Zachariah. She was talking about me. "...and why are you standing there like a Greek statue with that silly look on your face? Mary? Mary!"

I pulled myself back to the conversation at hand, and somehow managed to say, "I just can't imagine old Elizabeth being pregnant ... and, I guess ... what I think is ... that ... if that poor woman is blessed in her old age, ... I should go and give her a hand until the baby is born."

Much to my relief, Mother agreed!

I left as soon as I could to see Elizabeth. I had to know with certainty whether or not she was pregnant. My parents saw to it that I was attached to a caravan that would assure my safe passage, and I was soon on my way. It was a three-day walk down to Zachariah's home in the Sorek Valley. Although I was in the company of a number of people, I did have time to think when the others were not wanting to know what was on my mind or where I was going and why. As I walked along enjoying the scenery, I thought about all the implications of my encounter with the angel. Could I be pregnant, even though I am still a virgin? What if I am, and my parents and Joseph don't believe me? I knew my life could fall apart completely, but in the midst of all my concerns, I was filled with a sense of peace.

We finally arrived at Jerusalem, the destination for the caravan, but a few of us went on to the small village of Ein Kerem about five miles to the west. Ein Kerem was a quiet, peaceful place. Each time I came here, I had to remind myself that this was the poor South.[3] The hillsides were rich with lush vineyards, and a spring kept the countryside greener than one would expect. When I was growing up, my family had journeyed here several times, and I had always loved it. This village was a part of my childhood, a second home.

I saw old Zachariah standing in the door of the house when I got near. I called out to him, and hearing my voice, he walked out to meet me. He did not speak, for he could not, but he became very emotional when he recognized me. As I studied his face, I suddenly realized that this old couple needed me! I had come to see if what I had heard was true and had imagined arriving here, having my feet washed, getting some rest, and being catered to and babied by this couple. That was the way it had always been, but this time it was different! They needed me. Zachariah's eyes softened as he saw that I was beginning to understand. His face showed both joy and relief—joy that I had come, and relief that another woman was here to help with his now moody wife! I had no doubt that the shame of being pregnant at her age was keeping Elizabeth inside. On the other hand, she must be experiencing great joy at finally having a child after all

---

3. The southern part of Israel was poorer, because the land consisted of rocky hills, and soil was sparse. When vineyards were planted, soil actually had to be carried up from the valleys below and dumped behind rock terrace walls that were built on the hillside. The North was not as hilly or as rocky and consequently was wealthier (except for Nazareth).

these years. What a mix of emotions she must be experiencing!

"I guess Elizabeth's been hard to live with," I laughed, looking at Zachariah and feeling the warmth of all the love we had shared through the years. "Once the child is born, and the shame is over, she'll be all right," I added softly.

I could see his face relax, knowing that someone understood, so I reassured him. "I'm here to help, and I'll stay as long as you need me."

Upon hearing that, tears formed in Zachariah's eyes, and he stretched out his arms and gathered me in, nearly smothering me with his gratitude. "I'd do anything for you two," I whispered to him.

He was just releasing me when I heard Elizabeth's voice from inside the house, "Zachariah! Zachariah?! Where are you?"

He looked at me questioningly, his lips pursed. "Yes," I said, "I'll go in and deal with Elizabeth. Sounds like she's having a rough day." Saying I would help with Elizabeth gave me confidence and reassured Zachariah as well. He stood a little straighter, as he sent me into the house alone.

Slipping into the house, I saw Elizabeth sitting with her head down. She looked so alone and dejected! "Elizabeth?" I said quietly, suddenly unsure of what I should do. I was just a young teenager. Would I be able to minister to this fifty-five-year-old woman?![4] As I spoke, I saw Elizabeth catch her breath. Her hand jerked up onto her bulging belly and lay there. I wondered if she were going to stop breathing altogether when she looked up at me, her eyes aglow.

"Oh, Mary," she cried in a loud voice, "You're pregnant! You've been blessed and your baby is blessed![5] How is it that you've come to visit me, my dear child? You are the mother of my Lord!" Looking down at the

---

4. The life expectancy for women in Jesus' day was about forty, so Elizabeth, who according to tradition was about fifty-five at this time, was really quite old.

5. Biblically speaking, a blessing is a conferring and transferring of beneficial power. For example, when Aaron was first given the words of the Aaronic Blessing, "The Lord bless you and keep you...," God promised that whenever those words were spoken over the people they would be blessed, that is given power to live as God's people. When a woman in Bible times became pregnant, she would say she was blessed, that the power of God had been transferred to her in the gift of life. Blessings were usually given by words, which the ancients considered to have magical qualities (i.e. God said, "Let there be light!" and there was light. Likewise, if a person said, "I love you," the words have an effect on you.(Magical?)). Mary was blessed both by the words of the angel and the power of God which covered her and created a pregnancy within her. Her baby was blessed because of the power that was his. That power became evident later in his life.

hand lying on her belly, she laughed and shook her head. As she looked up again, I saw tears of joy in her eyes. "As soon as I heard your voice, my baby leaped for joy!"

Elizabeth and I both knew the stories of our ancestral mother Rebekah. When she was pregnant with her twins, Jacob and Esau had both leaped in her womb; Esau, the rascal, when she passed a pagan shrine, and Jacob, the holy child, when she passed a holy shrine or altar![6] Now Elizabeth knew, without being told, that I was pregnant with the Messiah, because her child had leaped for joy, sensing the presence of the true holy shrine, the true altar, the only true blessing for all people, the Lord, growing within me!

"And blessed are you who believed all the words that God sent to you, for everything you were told will come true and be completed in time!" Elizabeth leaned back, a contented look on her face.

I knew that I was blessed, for I could feel the power of God at work in me. Since the days of Adam and Eve, God had led his people down through history, paying the bride price again and again, in order to have an intimate relationship with his people. Now he was creating within me a life that would reveal to people the true nature of God by paying a bride price that would be enough for all time. From now on an intimate relationship with God would be possible for all who would have it. My child would be the fulfillment of centuries of hope. Through me, God was about to be made visible and to accomplish wondrous works! I was so filled with joy at Elizabeth's words, that I began to sing. Words similar to those Hannah had sung when she learned that she would become the mother of Samuel, came to my mind.

"Through my life, others will see clearly what God is like!" I sang. "God who has made my life complete, has filled me with joy, for he has seen my humiliation, my poverty, my low social standing, but most especially, he has seen my position as his slave!"[7]

Throughout our history, God had been known to choose those of low standing and raise them up. This he had now done with me, and I would continue to be his slave. A slave is not even a person without the master whom he or she must serve with complete obedience. The master

---

6. A story from the oral tradition recorded in the Midrash. The Midrash was known by all and was considered equal in authority to scripture. The scripture was not interpreted apart from the oral tradition.

7. The Greek word "doulas" should be translated as slave, rather than servant.

is all! The slave has no rights, no needs, no wants. The master has all rights, and his needs and wants are the only ones that matter! God was my master—and oh, what a Master he was! I was nothing without Him, but I was a wonder with Him! And it was with wonder that I suddenly realized that, because of what God had created in me, I would be remembered down through the ages from generation to generation. I would rank with Sarah and Hannah and Esther and all my other great foremothers! I sang on.

"From now on, all generations will consider me blessed, because the Mighty One did great things to me. His name is holy and holy is the compassion and pity he has shown down through the ages to those who held him in reverence, respecting and fearing him." God's name was so holy, I could not even speak it. It meant, "I am," and as every name pointed to the innermost nature of the person who carried it, so this name spoke to the essence of God. God simply is! Before time began, God was. Throughout all time, God existed and continues to exist. After time ends, God will still be the same. Because God is the great "I am," he is able to extend himself to us, unite with sinners, show pity and compassion and still remain steadfast, steady, never changing, undiminished by our sinfulness or by the giving of himself. So, it is possible for the love and mercy of "I am" to be extended to all people down through the ages.

"With his arm, God did mighty things. He scattered people whose lives showed their heartfelt belief that they were better than others."

By his mighty arm, God had created the world and all that is in it. By his mighty arm, God had claimed my people as his own, and freed them from slavery in Egypt. In all the great things that he did, God never chose the people you would have expected Him to choose! He chose those who were lowly, the humiliated. Our people were nothing but slaves who could not free themselves, yet God chose them to bring the greatest event in all history, an event that would give people an inner freedom and healing that was born from the unconditional forgiveness of all their sins, that reunited them with their Creator and enabled them to live and relish life to the fullest! And now, he had chosen me and by his mighty arm had created a pregnancy in me! God could have used a princess or the daughter of the High Priest to mother the Messiah, but instead he chose me! I was no one of significance, although I thought I had everything. I was betrothed to a wonderful man and excited about the future, but then suddenly, I was not only a poor maid from a poverty level village in an occupied land, but I was pregnant and unwed—an unspeakable condition in our culture. Then I really understood what it was to be lowly, to be humiliated! But from that humiliation, God brought me up to the highest heights. I would be an exalted one, and so would Elizabeth! She had held an honorable position among our people. She was married to a good priest, although he was certainly not well known. God had brought her down first through the shame of being barren, of being unable to carry out her function as a woman in our culture, and then through the shame of a pregnancy when she was old and past her time. She, too, would be exalted and remembered as the mother of a prophet. God always filled the hunger of those who recognized his greatness and trusted in him. But those who trusted only in themselves, God sent away with spirits that were still hungering and thirsting, although for what, they did not know.

I sang on. "The powerful, he pulled down from thrones. The lowly, he raised up high. Those who were hungering, he satisfied with good things, but the wealthy he sent out empty handed." I had desired to be God's humble slave, and now he was using me to bring the Promise to Israel. "He has come to the aid of his child—his servant—Israel, remembering mercy as he promised to our fathers—to Abraham and his seed unto the age." My song finished, I went to Elizabeth and, sitting down beside her, I put my arms around her. Elizabeth told me the story of all that had happened to her and Zachariah, and I told her all that had happened to me. Neither of us was alone with her secret any longer. It was such a relief, and we both cried for joy. Poor old Zachariah peeked through the door about this time, and when we saw the worried look on his face, we burst into laughter! He came in, now laughing himself, and when we had all been drained of our seriousness and refreshed by laughter, I offered to prepare supper. As I built a little fire to cook over, I marveled at having so much in common with Elizabeth in spite of the fact that she was an elderly woman married to a priest, and I was a teenager, betrothed to a carpenter.

The time in Ein Kerem went by quickly. I took over most of Elizabeth's duties, so that she could concentrate on preparing for the baby. When it was almost time for John's birth, other women from the priestly class arrived to help with the delivery and the aftercare that Elizabeth would need, so I decided to return home. I had gained a lot of strength from Elizabeth and Zachariah, and in a way, I was reluctant to leave. But, I was now more than three months into my own pregnancy, and I knew that eventually I would have to face Joseph. It was time to return to Nazareth. As I started toward home, I pondered what lay ahead. If ever I needed God's courage, it was now. Whenever I thought about telling Joseph that I was pregnant, my stomach knotted up, and I thought that I could not see this through. But, as I walked toward home with nothing to occupy me but my thoughts and prayers, my feelings slowly changed. I knew that I could survive what lay ahead, because God would see me through. Eventually, a sense of security settled in, in spite of the reality that lay ahead. I could be stoned if Joseph so chose, but he was a good man, and I was certain that he would not choose that horrible death for me! If only Joseph would believe what I had to tell him, but he would probably think that I had been unfaithful. I loved him so much, and I could not imagine living my life without him. Would he believe me? But then as I leaned on God and trusted him to handle things, peace came over me, and, although I did not know how it would all work out, I was sure that it would.

If I could just have hung onto that confidence, life would have been so much easier in the years that lay ahead.

CHAPTER 3

Joseph Learns the Truth

When I got home from visiting Elizabeth, Mother was anxious to hear all the news from the South. I did my best to be excited and give her all the details, but I had only one thing on my mind—telling Joseph about the pregnancy. I would tell him before I told anyone else, and I just wanted it done! Mother could see that something was bothering me, and she puzzled and prodded trying to find out what it was, but having no luck, she returned to trying to get me to talk about my trip. I could not concentrate, and our conversation was certainly less than she had hoped it would be. It was not often that a family from Nazareth sent a daughter all the way to Ein Kerem to help an elderly woman of the priestly class, who was pregnant, and whose husband was unable to speak because of an angel. Mother wanted stories to tell at the well,[1] and I was sorry that I was not doing better providing her with them. I tried, but then thoughts of Joseph would pop into my mind, and everything else would be swept away. I tried using my weariness from the trip as an excuse, but Mother knew it was much more than that, and she wanted to know what it was, or she wanted to hear about the trip! Whichever I chose was fine, but she was quickly growing frustrated. Finally, seeing that I was near tears, she decided to leave me alone.

It was then that I heard Joseph coming. He had learned that I was back in town, had taken a break from his work, and was coming to see if I had made the journey safely. Mother hurried to meet Joseph at the door. As he spoke greetings to her, my heart pounded, and my stomach tightened into a knot. A sense of unreality gripped me, as I silently begged God to get me through the next hour. Joseph looked toward me and seeing my eyes, he knew immediately that something was wrong. He looked questioningly at my mother, who simply shrugged and threw up her hands.

---

1. A lot of socializing went on at the well where women met and talked.

By now, she was worried that whatever had happened might cause Joseph to divorce me, so when Joseph took my arm to lead me outside, she was more than ready to let us go.

Joseph took me around to the side of the house, where I had seen the angel. I remember thinking that God had led him there, because it would be easier for me to tell him the story right there where it had happened. I began speaking immediately, even before we sat down. Shaking words came bursting from my mouth, betraying the silent fear within me.

"There was an angel here!" I said, looking to see Joseph's reaction. "It was standing right here where we are."

Joseph's lips showed a small indulgent smile. He took my arm and moved close to the stone bench, beside which I had rested on that day just a few months ago. Raising his eyebrows, he waited for me to go on. My mouth was going dry and my heart drummed in my ears, as I tried to think what would help him believe me, but his patronizing look shook me, so that now my words tumbled out awkwardly.

"Well, it was ... it looked like a man, but ...it kind of ... was here ... and then—it wasn't ... and ... well, I was sitting back here ... ," I pointed to the ground, "Umm ... thinking about you." My cheeks flushed. It was a bold thing for me to say, but I wanted him to know. Maybe it would help when I told him I was pregnant.

"Sounds like you've got too many angels on your mind, my beloved Mary," Joseph said gently, sitting down and pulling me down beside him. "I heard about Zachariah's angel. Did you have a difficult time in Ein Kerem? I shouldn't have allowed you to go. I've missed you. It's time we moved in together and made our decision about going ahead with the marriage."[2] I could see that he was not taking me seriously.

"No... no, it was before I heard about Zachariah." The sense of unreality was gone. This was real. Joseph did not believe me. What could I say? My mind struggled to put together something that would not send him away.

Joseph laid his hand on my arm. "Just say it, Mary! Tell me what's going on in that head of yours. You're beginning to scare me."

I took a deep breath, trying to calm myself. My racing heart slowed. "There was an angel," I said definitively. Joseph's smile left his face, and he

2. This is a reference to the time during the year of betrothal when the couple lived together in a non-sexual relationship in the presence of relatives prior to making the final decision to go ahead with the marriage.

looked at me quietly and seriously.

I took my eyes from his face. I would never get the truth out, if I continued watching his reactions.

"The angel stood there, and told me not to be afraid. It said I was blessed and special, and I would be remembered like Rachel and Sarah." I was rambling. "It said … I was to be the mother of the Messiah." I moved my tongue around my mouth, fighting the dry stickiness that was making it so difficult to form the words I needed to say.

"I thought he meant that you and I would have a son that would be the Messiah … but that's not what he meant." I felt Joseph's body tense up next to me, and, considering what I had to say, I thought that maybe this was as close as I would ever get to him. He was obviously beginning to suspect what I was about to say, and he remained silent. Unable to handle his silence, I went on.

"So, I said, 'How can this be, because I… umm… hadn't… uhh … done anything with a man.'" I paused. How could I even think of talking about such things with Joseph? Nevertheless, I had to tell him! I went on. "Anyway, he said that God would cover me with his Spirit, and I would be pregnant even though I'm a… uh… virgin." I rubbed my forehead, trying to find strength. I would simply have to force myself to go on. I had the empty, hopeless feeling that no matter what I had to say, Joseph would not believe me. But I had to tell him anyway.

From Joseph, there was silence.

"And so… and so… I said I wanted to be God's slave… and I meant it… and I said whatever God wanted… 'Let it be!' because if God could create the universe, he could create a baby… in me. And I am… pregnant, that is…"

Silence. Oh, dear God, help me. I feel so empty, so desolate. He does not believe me.

"So then I heard that Elizabeth was pregnant—well … the angel told me first … and then Mother said it, too … so, I asked if I could go help her … Elizabeth, that is." I fought the dryness in my mouth. Sweat ran down my sides from beneath my arms. "So I went … and I didn't even have to tell Elizabeth about my baby, because her baby will be a prophet, and he jumped when he heard my voice, like … like Jacob in Rachel … and, and Elizabeth said, 'How is it that you've come to visit me? You are the mother of my… Lord!'"

Silence was all I heard.

"The angel said I shouldn't be afraid... but I am." My head was hanging nearly to my chest by now. I was terrified. I was so afraid of losing Joseph... so afraid of not having him there with me, to help me through...

Silence.

I just sat, waiting. Surely, he would say something soon. The long trip home and now this conversation with Joseph had drained my strength. I wondered if I had the energy to keep breathing.

The silence went on too long. If only Joseph would speak! I looked at his face with uncertainty. Joseph sat without saying a word, staring at the ground in front of him. Then his solemn eyes turned to me and watched me closely. His face was sad, but revealed little else. Nervously, I pointed to the place where the angel had stood.

"It was right there," I said, my voice growing desperate. I hoped this bit of information would move Joseph to words. I watched him. I could not bear this silence, but Joseph's eyes did not change, and he did not speak. His face maintained the same, solemn look. I studied him for a few seconds longer, and as I did, I prayed that God would send the angel again! I needed it to help me convince Joseph!

When Joseph did not move and remained silent, I nervously moved on to telling more about the trip to Elizabeth's and Zachariah's place. I could not stand the silence, so I threw out whatever came to mind, looking at him briefly with wondering eyes every few seconds. He remained silent as I related everything I could think of about my adventure to Ein Kerem. When I finally fell silent—I had nothing left to say—Joseph looked at me again for a long time. Then standing slowly and shaking his head sadly, he said, "Mary, you don't really expect me to believe all that, do you? No one thinks you are more special than I do—but an angel? And because of what it had to say, you're pregnant? You really didn't have to go to all this trouble. You know that I love you. I would never have you stoned, if that's what you're worried about!"

My soul let out a silent scream, "Noooo! My God, where are you?" My heart pounded in my ears once again, and I sat there by the edge of the house, waiting. He simply had to say the words I wanted to hear him say: "It's all right, Mary. I believe you. I know you would never make up something like this."

Instead, the words I dreaded broke through the wall I had built against them. "I'll go to the elders tomorrow and get a quiet divorce. No one needs to hear much about it. Our wedding just won't happen. You're free to marry the young man—whoever he is."

I sat looking at him in disbelief. "I'd rather be stoned!" I whispered to myself. His back was to me. He stood quietly for a moment, then turned around quickly! The expression on his face had changed. I now saw anger and shock born of a new thought. I braced myself. For a split second, I thought he was going to have me stoned, after all. "I didn't mean it," I whispered.

But the new thought that now exploded from his mouth was not at all what I expected. "Was it a Roman?" he demanded.

We both knew what he meant. I would not have been the first Jewish virgin raped by the soldiers who occupied our land. I guess it had just occurred to Joseph that I might have made up the story about the angel to protect him—to keep him from striking out in retaliation, and possibly losing his life or, at the very least, ending up in prison. It had happened to others, and once the Romans dealt with the men who sought revenge, the women were in much worse straits than before. There was then no one to provide for them, and there was always the possibility of a child on the way. And there was no way for a woman to earn a living, except by prostitution. Because of one action taken by one soldier, the woman would go from looking forward to being a Jewish wife and mother, to being condemned to living the rest of her life as a sinner—the name given to prostitutes. There was no winning once a person tangled with the Romans. They did as they pleased.

I shook my head; my eyes filled with tears. "No, Joseph," I said quietly. "It was not a Roman." He shook his head now, and seemingly convinced, he turned and walked slowly away. I wanted to go after him, to grab his arm and pull him back. I wanted to cry out and beg him to believe me. I wanted him to stay, but all I could do was sit and watch him go. I hadn't thought it would work out this way. What was I supposed to do now? Bring God's son into the world and raise him by myself? How could I? My mother would surely disown me! Would I have any option other than prostitution, if I wanted to eat and feed my baby? How could I do that and be the mother of the Messiah? If only Joseph had been willing to marry me, people would have thought the baby was his son. He would have been a good father, and being older and well established, he could have provided a stable home. If Joseph didn't believe me, maybe I was crazy! I sat alone on the bench for a long time trying to pray, trying to think. Finally, exhausted and emotionally spent, too drained even to weep, I went back into the house.

I tried to act cheerful when Mother asked where Joseph had gone, but I didn't fool her. She could see that something was terribly wrong, and I knew she wanted to help. But if Joseph didn't believe me, and if I now doubted myself, how could I expect her to understand? It was asking too much, even for my mother. I decided she would have to wait until morning to hear the story. I was just not up to telling her tonight, and besides, the only thing I was sure about at this point was—that I was pregnant.

I tossed and turned all night. I had really believed that everything would work out. Whatever would I do now? I drifted off briefly just before dawn, but I didn't sleep long. The first rays of light roused me, and I arose and dressed. My parents would have to hear the story today. If I could convince my mother, perhaps she would handle my father.

I stepped outside to let the cool morning air refresh me. I loved the way the dew hung on everything around and its freshness filled the air. Soon the sun would burn off the mist and the dew, but for now the life-giving moisture was there, as we knew it would be every day of the dry season, reminding us of our life-giving God and His faithful daily presence with his people. I stood musing about the faithfulness of God for a short time as I soaked in the cool moist air. It was soothing to my burning eyes and achy head. The long sleepless night had taken its toll on me. My body longed to lie down and rest, but I knew there would be no rest until I told my parents, and I really doubted that I would be able to rest even then. I did not care to imagine what they would say. Then my thoughts were pulled back to God. Our God had always been faithful to us as a people. Even when it appeared that He had not, still all things worked together for God's purpose in the end. God would be faithful to me as an individual, too. I knew it was true, and as I was comforted by this thought, I relaxed a little.

The tension had only just begun to drain from me when I heard Joseph's voice. "Mary." I had been resting my eyes and was so absorbed in my thoughts, that I did not hear his approaching footsteps. Now, when I opened my eyes, there was Joseph's smiling face directly in front of me. "I knew you'd be out here," he said, puffing a little as he spoke. He had obviously hurried to get here. "I couldn't wait to see you," he went on. "I know I hurt you badly when I didn't believe you, but Mary, can you blame me?! That was quite a story you had to tell." He took hold of my arms with his strong hands and smiled down into my eyes. I returned his gaze with wonder. My throat was growing tight and aching with the potential for tears. I could see that Joseph had changed his mind about my story. Joy began to swell in my belly, and I fell into his arms. I never should have doubted! I had known that God would take care of things, but I had forgotten as I tried to handle things myself. Thank God, that His graciousness and faithfulness continue, even when we forget that it is there for us!

"Your angel visited me last night in a dream." Joseph leaned his face into my hair and murmured into my ear. Our embrace was already breaking all cultural standards, but neither of us cared. "He said I was not to worry or be afraid—that you were telling me the truth—that you were blessed with God's own Son—that I should not divorce you, but take you as my wife and care for you. Can you ever forgive me?"

"You're here now," I sobbed as the joy and relief spilled out and ran in tears down my cheeks. "That's all that matters." He believed me! Thank God, he believed me!

Joseph gave me a squeeze. "Do your parents know?" he asked. I shook my head. "Let's go and tell them that you're pregnant. After all, we are betrothed. It simply means we won't have the wedding we were planning. You can move in with me without all the formalities. We can begin our life together right away—a life of being there for each other. Oh, Mary, it will be so good to have you near, and we'll have plenty of time to talk privately then. I can't imagine being responsible for raising the Messiah. I'm to be his father! I'll teach him my carpentry trade… and God's Word …" I looked up into Joseph's face. He looked stunned. "I will be responsible for teaching God's Word to the Messiah?" he breathed. His face was filled with so many emotions, it was hard to recognize them all. There was the wonder of believing something unbelievable—of being given responsibility far beyond anything either of us had ever dreamed we were capable of handling. There was the joy of sensing God's presence, the peace that had strangely settled over both of us. I could see the love that he had for me, the relief of not having to go through a divorce, and the determination to rise to this occasion and do his best. I settled my head back on his chest. Thank

God for Joseph! It took a very special man to accept things as he had, and actually be excited about it. He was indeed living up to his name, Joseph, son of Israel, faithful servant of God. He had continued in faithfulness through the harshest of trials.

Joseph held me for a while, and then we walked slowly into the house with our arms around one another. We would tell my parents together. They would be disappointed that we were not going to have the traditional week long wedding celebration, but it would also save a lot of money. They would assume that Joseph was the father of the baby, and Joseph would accept that responsibility. Since we were betrothed and a betrothal was a legal contract that could only be ended by divorce, people would assume, because I was with child, that we had already gone ahead and married one another. Becoming Joseph's wife in the eyes of the world was that simple, and I was relieved and comforted.

CHAPTER 4

Jesus is Born

People assumed that I was pregnant when Joseph simply came and paid the bride price and I followed him home without a big celebration. Then came the whispers and finger-counting as my pregnancy began to show, and the gossips began trying to figure out when the wedding really took place. Poor Mother was beside herself. But I was content. Being near Joseph and knowing his strength was such a comfort. He shared my secret, and he kept it a secret. His strong faith sustained him as other men nudged one another and smirked, accusing him of being the baby's father. He had not wavered in his faith since the angel had come to him in the dream, so when doubts came to me, I rested on his strength. I kept busy learning to run a household of my own and learning to be of help with Joseph's trade. I enjoyed being his wife and preparing for the baby's arrival.

In those days, I would see Mother at the well when I went for water. She got over being upset about the seeming indiscretion committed by Joseph and me, and actually got excited about the coming baby. I was glad she was nearby, and some days I was tempted to tell her about the angel, but I held back, thinking she would not believe me unless the angel came to her as it had to Joseph.

Life calmed down and things went smoothly for a time. I was growing heavy with the child and, although content, I was looking forward to having the birth behind me. It occurred to me that I would need a midwife, and when I mentioned it to Mother one day, I found that she was way ahead of me. She had been making inquiries at the well where all the women met, and was ready to tell me who was available. She suggested one woman in particular who was young enough to relate well to me and old enough to have had quite a bit of experience. Once I agreed, Mother was happy to go and make the arrangements on my behalf, and I was happy to have her do it.

So it was that life seemed settled and good, but then the news of the census came. Caesar Augustus had decreed—not requested, but decreed—that all the people of his realm were to go to the towns of their ancestors to be counted. Joseph's being a descendant of David meant that we would have to go to Bethlehem. But it was nearly time for me to deliver the child! The thought of the journey made me weary beyond words, but the emperor had decreed it! So, I began to plan what we would need for our journey. I gathered together some food. Wheat that was picked green and roasted was a popular item for travelers to eat along the way. Raisins would give us energy, and I had plenty of those put away for the year. I would take a little flour and oil, so I could bake bread on hot stones pulled from the campfire where we stopped for the night. I was packing these things into a basket when Joseph came in. He stood silently watching me for a bit, and then he spoke. "You know, Mary, you could stay here. It's so near your time. Your mother would be glad to keep you, and the midwife would be nearby if you needed her."

I went on with my packing, thinking about what Joseph had said. His proposal sounded good. Walking had grown difficult. I could hardly make it to the well anymore before my muscles would ache and complain about the child's weight bearing down upon them. But the thought of staying behind didn't feel right! I suddenly realized how much I had come to depend on Joseph. I could not imagine being without him now, even if I had to walk clear to Egypt! Only he and Elizabeth understood what was happening within me. Only they knew that I was carrying God's son. I needed to be near someone who shared my secret and believed that it was true. If Joseph had to go to Bethlehem, I would go with him.

I turned suddenly toward Joseph, catching him off guard. "I'm going with you, Joseph!" I said, and there was such a certainty in my voice that Joseph offered no resistance. He simply smiled and nodded. "I am, after all, a Hebrew woman," I added, smiling back at him and savoring the use of the word woman to refer to myself. "Hebrew women have never let child bearing slow them down." We laughed together, and Joseph came over and gave me a hug.

"I'm very proud of you," he said tenderly, cupping my chin in his hand and looking into my eyes. "I didn't really want to leave you here. I don't want to miss the child's birth. I want to begin looking out for him from his earliest hour." He paused for a moment, serious. Then he grinned. "Besides, I've gotten used to having you around." We shared another long embrace.

The next morning we left for Bethlehem. Along the way, we found a couple of families who were also of David's line, and we fell in with them. They had some older family members with them who needed to walk slowly, as did I. So, we began what would normally be a three to four-day journey, with the hope of making it in four or five days. I walked. There was no donkey to ride, for donkeys were highly valued animals[1] usually owned by several poor families together. People seldom rode the beasts, since the donkey was not kept for riding, but for labor the men could not do. All the owners shared in providing food for the animal and benefited from the work it could do. Besides, it was a very rough, jolting ride on the back of a donkey, not a ride that a pregnant woman would consider, unless she was trying to encourage the baby to make an early appearance into the world!

It was a long and tiring walk. The days seemed to never end, and I lay down exhausted each night. I had made my own choice, and I was glad I had decided to come with Joseph, but I longed to see Bethlehem and the possibility of a few days rest before we started home again.

When we got to Bethlehem, it was no surprise that the inn was full. Bethlehem had a population of only about 1,000 people nestled inside its city walls, so there was just one inn. Within that one inn, all the guests ate and slept together in one big room. I had prayed that my time would not come while we were staying in the inn! I could not imagine giving birth there?! So when the innkeeper told Joseph that there was no room in the inn itself, I was a little relieved, knowing Joseph would find some other place for me.

"But my wife is with child, and her time is near," I heard Joseph say. "She is having some pains already!"

"You can take shelter in the stable, if you like," the innkeeper offered.

"A stable?!" I thought smugly. "Joseph can do better for me and our son than a stable." Then another contraction started, and my body shuddered with pain. I looked up at Joseph. He saw what was happening and

---

1. The value of a donkey is seen in Exodus 13:13 where all firstborn animals belong to God and are to be sacrificed except a donkey, which may be redeemed.

with a worried look, he nodded to the innkeeper, who directed us to a natural cave in the side of the hill that dropped down behind the inn. The cave was cold and damp, but it offered shelter from the winter rains that had come upon us. It was not my choice of places to bring my baby into the world, but it was better than the crowded inn. If I did give birth, at least I would be alone.

And I did give birth. And I was alone. And I was frightened. I was fifteen[2] years old, and, although others had told me about their own experiences with childbirth, none of what they said fit exactly with what I was experiencing. So I was indeed afraid, but this was not a time when I could allow myself the luxury of letting fear rule my thoughts or actions. If I panicked and wasted time wishing for the midwife that my mother had engaged, it would not change the facts. I was alone. And I was in labor. I would not panic. I would tend to things myself.

I knew that Joseph was waiting patiently outside, and I took comfort in that. He was tired from the long journey and would have liked to be in the cave and out of the rain, but Hebrew men never helped with childbirth or even witnessed it. He would wait outside in spite of the weather, unless, of course, I got into trouble. Then he would break with tradition and come to me. He had offered to go off and look for a midwife, but there was no guarantee that he would find one, and with him gone, I would be utterly alone. I had asked him to stay.

The birth went smoothly and fairly quickly for a first baby. Still, by the time Jesus was finally born, I had learned all about the pain and exhaustion of childbirth. Nevertheless, I tended to myself and cared for the child as I had been taught to do.

After I had wiped Jesus clean and knew that he was breathing properly, I looked him over. He seemed fine, so I took strips of cloth, swaddling cloths we called them, and wrapped him snugly to warm him and to help him feel secure in the big open world he had just entered. When I was finished, I looked around for a place to put him, and finding no other spot, I laid him in the manger there in the stable. It seemed cruel to place a newborn babe in a feed trough carved from a big piece of cold limestone, but the animals' food would cushion him, and he would be safely off the floor while I rested. As I looked back many years later, I could see in that child lying on that cold stone wrapped in strips of cloth, a foreshadowing

---

2. Girls married at puberty—13 to 16 years of age.

of the day when he would once again be wrapped in strips of cloth and laid on a cold stone shelf at the end of his life. Thank God, I did not know then how his death would come, or that I would be there to see him die. It would have been more than I could bear, to know that one day my baby would suffer so, and I would be unable to do anything but watch.

For now, it was enough that I had tended to the baby and myself. Now I could rest. Leaning against the manger, I slid to my knees and rested my head on my arms. I was so tired, and I was aching from the birth … and from the cold and dampness … and from being alone. It was dark, and I remember feeling so discouraged. Was this the way the Messiah would come? In a borrowed animal cave? In the cold dark night? Without help? How much worse could it get?! Perhaps I had only dreamed of the angel, and this was not the Messiah at all! Maybe none of it was true. Maybe I had been raped by a soldier and had blocked it out of my mind. Tears came, and I wept quietly. Joseph, knowing the birth was accomplished, came into the stable, and seeing me in tears, knelt beside me and took me in his arms, even though this was against tradition. I was unclean from the birth and touching me made him unclean, too. But Joseph held me. He was so good that way. He loved God's word and the laws, but he was compassionate, and he recognized that the laws were for our good. They were guides for living and not just rules that we kept simply because they were there. So, if I needed comfort, he would comfort me in spite of the laws. For him, the law of love cast its light on all other laws, superceding them at times, magnifying them at other times, but always interpreting them.

When Joseph felt confident that I was doing better, he gently lowered me down onto the bed that I had fixed for myself on the floor beside the manger. Then, pausing to look at the child, he too found a place to rest. I lay looking at him. He was an amazing man, and in some ways I envied him. One visit from the angel had settled things completely for Joseph. He looked at his situation, decided what he needed to do, and simply went on. That amazed me because I was one who thought and wondered and doubted, always seeking more knowledge and a deeper understanding. We were different in that way. So, I lay resting, questioning within myself whether the Messiah would really be born in such dreadful circumstances, while Joseph peacefully fell asleep.

I was trying to relax, and had just closed my eyes, when a presence caused me to start. My eyes flew open and there, silhouetted in the door of the cave, stood several shepherds. The small fire that burned in the cave threw golden flickers of light mixed with shadows onto the shepherds' faces. I was already feeling sorry for myself, being so far from home, hurting, exhausted, feeling forgotten by God, and now shepherds! They were such a disreputable bunch and well known for their thievery. You had to keep things put away when they were in the fields nearby. And they were irreligious. They could not attend the synagogue for watching their sheep, they said. And now here they were! I was so frightened. I raised up on my hands to a half sitting position as the tears began to roll quickly down my cheeks without so much as a sound of a sob. Joseph, awakened by the sound of the rustling of the animal skins that the shepherds wore to shield themselves from the rain, quickly assessed the situation and moved between me and the shepherds, so he could shield me.

Then one of the shepherds began to speak, and the tale he told was a wonder. He began by telling about an angel who had come bringing to all the shepherds who were out in the field that night the news of my son's birth. Then he told of an army of angels that had come and had sung to them. As he described the scene, it was almost as though I could see it before my very eyes. The shepherds had been out on the hillsides[3] near Bethlehem watching over their sheep to keep them safe, as they always did, when a messenger of God, an angel, had come quite suddenly and had stood right there in front of them in the field, and at the same time, there was a strange light all around. The shepherds sensed that God was very near, and they were frightened nearly to death. They knew what other people thought of them, and not thinking too highly of themselves, they were not sure what God wanted with them, but they assumed the worst! But the angel told them not to be afraid, because he had just come to bring them good news about an event that would soon offer to all people an unexplainable happiness and a sense of well-being that would come when all else in the world said that there should be no joy or peace! A Savior—a Messiah—had been born in Bethlehem, and if they went there, they could find him in a manger. Then all of a sudden a whole army of

3. The hillsides right outside Bethlehem are riddled with limestone caves. Shepherds still use those caves as sheep folds. A stone wall encloses a small area outside each cave, and when the sheep are in the fold at night, the shepherd sleeps in a sitting position in the opening of the wall in order to keep out any creature that would harm the sheep. (The shepherd is the gate. When Jesus said, "I am the gate," he was making reference to this.) The caves are close together, and the shepherds could easily have talked to one another as they watched over their sheep.

angels appeared in the sky and started singing something like, "Glory to God in the highest, and peace to his people on earth." When the angels left, and it was dark again, every one sat in shocked silence for a while. What the angel had told them seemed too good to be true! The angel had said that the good news was for all people. That meant shepherds, too! And God had sent the angel to shepherds! What did this mean? Was shepherding to be restored to a position of honor as it had once been, as when Abraham was a shepherd? Could it be? If this were real, it could mean a new life for these outcast men and their families, because it would mean not only that God loved them and accepted them, but that perhaps people would accept them, too, and they wouldn't have to be outcasts anymore.

Then one of the shepherds had whispered, almost reluctantly, as if not wanting to break the spell, "Did you see what I saw?" needing—not wanting—needing to know if it were real.

That shepherd heard affirmative murmurings all around him, so he said a little more boldly, "Let's go into Bethlehem and see if it's true!" That was all it took to break the spell completely. Within an instant, every member of that little band of shepherds was running excitedly, foolishly toward Bethlehem. Foolishly, because those fields around Bethlehem are more limestone rock than grass, and in the bleak, black, darkness of that drizzly December night, the shepherds could be heard slipping and tripping, and crying out at a cracked shin or a stunned hand that had come down hard on a rock in an attempt to break a shepherd's fall. They were drunk with joy and hope.

When they had come to Bethlehem, they had sobered a little. There was no sign of life. The little town was sleeping as though nothing had happened. The shepherds hesitated wondering ... after all, would God have told shepherds this news about the Messiah and not the good religious people of the town? It did not make sense! However, the shepherds hesitated only briefly before pushing on. They could never have just imagined such news as this! It had to be true. Why no one else seemed to know, they did not know, but they were determined not to let the ignorance of others stop them. They pushed on quietly. If they were caught in town, it could go hard for them. No one trusted a shepherd—especially one wandering into town at night. They peered cautiously into the back rooms of homes where animals were kept and found nothing. Then, refusing to give up, they headed for the inn. There were a lot of visitors in town for the census, and perhaps the new parents were visitors rather than residents of Bethlehem. When they got to the inn, they saw that there was no light inside, but what they did see was a light coming from behind and below the inn, apparently from the cave where the innkeeper kept his animals. They approached the cave and looking in, saw the baby in a manger just as the angel had said.

Looking at the child, the shepherd told me how he knew that they had found the right child, not because it was wrapped in strips of cloth as all babies were, but because it was lying in a manger. To think that I had felt bad about putting him there!

By the time the shepherd finished telling his story, my discouragement had slipped away. With renewed confidence and my heart so full of the story he had told, without thinking, I asked, "Would you like to hold the baby?" I immediately regretted this impetuous invitation and was not even sure why I had said it. Shepherds were not a clean lot, and in this rainy season, he was wet as well. This smeary, smelly shepherd was now invited to hold my precious new child.

"Maybe he'll say no," I thought, without much hope of it turning out that way. I watched as he slipped off the wet animal skin that he was wearing over his clothing, leaned over the manger, and gently scooped the child into his obviously experienced but dirty arms. Then a strange thing happened. As I watched that old shepherd, his rough, weather-beaten face began to soften. The arrogance born of rejection and oppression began to drain away. A look of joy and peace filled the man's face and then, with a start, I recognized in his face the same security that had filled me as I had trudged back to Nazareth after visiting Elizabeth. Tears filled my eyes again as I realized that this was what my son had come to bring. It was from him—yet unborn—that peace and security had come to me, a young teenager on that hot dry day, even though I was pregnant with a child that was not my betrothed's, in a culture that dealt ruthlessly with such people. And it was from him—a tiny baby—that this old shepherd, an outcast since he had begun training to become a shepherd as a small boy,[4] found peace on this cold, wet night. What could this mean? Who was I to have a part in the life of this child who would bring such changes into human lives? If this was the effect that he was to have on all whom he

4. Children began training to become shepherds as soon as they were weaned, usually about three years of age. From that time on, they lived with the sheep under the tutelage of an older shepherd.

would meet, his life was bound to bring healing to many.

Imprisoned by my thoughts, I watched the shepherd putting the baby back into the manger, reluctantly, as though hoping I would say, "Oh, don't go." But I was anxious to have them all gone. I was exhausted from childbirth, though now strangely warmed. I wanted to be alone so I could think.

With a newfound dignity the man straightened himself and, with one last glance at the baby, he spoke thank-yous and goodbyes for the whole group, and slipping his wet outer garment over his head, he led the others out of the cave and disappeared into the darkness, leaving behind nothing but the sound of rain falling gently in the puddles outside.

When the shepherds were gone, I continued deep in thought. Such wondrous things were happening. I felt ashamed of having been so discouraged earlier. It was the shepherds' visit that had lifted a great burden from my shoulders, and I had not even wanted to see the shepherds … I was back on the path I needed to be on. This was God's son. He was to be great beyond my understanding. I knew now, that God would always give me what I needed to keep going in the face of all circumstances. It would continue to be so, I now realized, as it always had been. Pondering, I remembered that after the angel had come to bring me the initial shocking news, there was Elizabeth to affirm what the angel said. Then there was Joseph's change of attitude just when I was about to give up. Now the shepherds had come to reassure me that the Son of God could indeed be born in a stable, where he could be approached by the most unlikely and humblest of all of God's people, touching their lives by his presence and by the realization that it was in his presence that they belonged. God had been teaching me from the very beginning that He would always be in control and would always give me what I needed, even when things seemed the worst. The day would come too soon when I would need all the strength that I was accumulating through the hard times. Seeing my son crucified, and surviving as I saw him die, would take everything I had learned along with every ounce of stamina that God could give me. God was preparing me and would see me through.

CHAPTER 5

Old Simeon and Anna

The shepherds told everyone they met about the Messiah who was born in the stable. A few people came around after that, mostly other shepherds. There were only a few because hardly anyone, even other shepherds, would take a thieving sheep herder seriously when he said that he and the rest of his band had seen angels in the night, singing and telling them where to find the newborn Messiah. Most asked whose wine cellar had been pilfered that night and how much one had to drink in order to see such a sight, because they'd like to see it, too. When a few did venture to ask where they had found the Messiah and the shepherds answered, "In the stable behind the inn!" that clinched it.

"Of course God's son would be born in a stable! Where else would you look for royalty?!" the people jeered.

"In the first place," people reasoned in their chatter at the market place, "the whole story is so fantastic that it just doesn't make sense … in fact, it's amazing that a bunch of uneducated shepherds even came up with such a tale!"

"And in the second place," someone else jumped in, "what makes those shepherds think that anyone would believe that God would notify them about the birth of the Messiah instead of going to those who make no bones about being God's people? The priests, the scribes, or the Pharisees and Sadducees would obviously be the first to know."

"Yeah," cried another, "and people like young Bezelel,[1] just down the street. Everyone can hear him say his morning and evening prayers everyday!"

"And what about the merchant, Absalom?[2] We've all seen the offerings he loads up to take to the temple! God would surely tell him long

1. Fictitious character
2. Fictitious character

before a bunch of lowly shepherds!"

What didn't occur to these people, who thought only on a surface level about religion anyway, was that those who made such a show of their religion were not the ones to whom God would go. For one thing, their religious actions were often divisive among God's people. Some would look at all the rigid restrictions they chose to live with and say, "If that's what God is all about, I'll pass." Of course, that was just "proof" that these others were simply not God's people to begin with, and so the "religious ones" didn't think twice about their own actions. If the first division, which was unintentional, were not bad enough, there was an intentional division as well. It resulted from the belief that being near "sinners" would taint the "righteous ones."

By dividing God's people and by judging others, which is only God's prerogative, these highly religious people were themselves sinning. But they could not see it. They were convinced that they possessed God's truth and that the way they lived was the only right way! They had become so caught up in being righteous that they couldn't see that their righteousness had turned to sin. They just went on making decisions on God's behalf, shutting out God as they shut out people, even shutting out those inklings within themselves that suggested that, perhaps, they were not really right and that maybe there was a better way. Thus, they had become blind—so hardened that they were no longer able to recognize God's presence—as would become clear later on when Jesus began his ministry.

The shepherds, on the other hand, were an open book in which God could write. They had no preconceived ideas that God would have to overcome before He could get through to them. They needed a living faith that spoke to them in the midst of their harsh lives, and they had no reason to doubt that the Truth could claim them, coming to them in strange ways, even though they did not keep all the rules and regulations, which they had never learned anyway. So God had sent messengers to them, and they would tell the story, and if others did not believe, well... the shepherds knew! And they had learned long ago not to let what others thought bother them. Some of those who heard the shepherds' story looked into the yellowed eyes of that old shepherd who had held Jesus in his arms, and, having seen the changes that were wrought and the peace that lay deep within that weathered face, came to visit Jesus themselves, wanting that same peace and contentment.

We moved out of the stable into a house shortly after Jesus was born. The stable was a welcome temporary shelter, but it was not the sort of place where we wanted to stay for long. When Joseph located a house, we moved quickly. There I had time to rest and get used to being a mother before it was time to go up to the temple.

Following the forty days of purification after the birth of my son, it was necessary for me to go to the temple and make an offering in order to become ritually clean once again. Fortunately, when the time came, the rainy season was nearly over. The hard rains had come in November and December, as always, breaking up the hard soil and permitting the farmers to get their grain planted. Now the light rains of January and February had arrived, encouraging the sprouted grain to green the fields. It was a favorite time of year for me. The air was moist and fresh, the grapevines and other plants were returning to life. Only the fig trees seemed to hold out, stubbornly refusing to show their leaves until the rains had ended and summer was near.

The day we walked up to Jerusalem was beautiful. The clouds parted and the sun shone through, warming me as we walked in the early morning hours. This was the beginning of a new segment of my life. Today I would not just end my time of isolation. Today I would bring my first born—a son—to dedicate to God. Now I would join the ranks of the women of Israel. No longer would I be considered a child, or merely a female. I would now be known as "Mary, the mother of Jesus!" At last I would have an identity like other adults, and I felt so proud! "Mary, the mother of Jesus!" It sounded so wonderful in my head, that I said it out loud just to see how it felt, "Mary, the mother of Jesus!" Joseph squeezed my arm and smiled. I blushed. I had been so caught up in my thoughts that I had become unaware of him walking beside me. "Mary, the mother of Jesus!" I said again, louder this time, and with laughter. Joseph joined in, and we reveled in one another's presence as we pressed on toward Jerusalem as a family. Only God knew what that name would come to mean, although the events leading up to this day should have been a clue that "Mary, the mother of Jesus" was not a name that would be bestowed without cost.

Going to the temple was always exciting. It was a time that came all too infrequently for those of us who lived in Nazareth, far from our center of worship. Herod's temple was such a beautiful place.[3] I could remember journeying to it as a child, cresting the Mount of Olives, and seeing that gleaming white limestone building break into view. It nearly took my breath away each time we came. And as we drew near and entered into the temple area, I would be in such awe of actually being at God's house! It was like a dream! Each time I would stand quietly in wonder and it seemed the presence of God would wrap around me and embrace me until I thought I would burst with joy. It was an awesome experience, and one I longed to have again.

In addition to the feelings of awe and wonder and strength that overwhelmed me whenever we visited the temple, there was all the activity that created an air of excitement. There were the money changers selling temple money for people to use as offerings. Traders would be selling animals for sacrifices, while other people were herding in their own homegrown animals. The priests, pompous, proud, and finely clad, would be scurrying about with great dignity, performing their duties. Some people would be standing facing the east, heads up, eyes open, arms lifted and outstretched, opening themselves to God in prayer. Others had trumpets sounded before them to announce the arrival of the great offerings they brought, while still others slipped in quietly and humbly to give what small sums they were able.

I thought of the offerings as we walked towards Jerusalem and felt again the humiliation of our circumstances. My cleansing required that we offer a lamb for a burnt offering, and a turtledove or pigeon as a sin offering to complete my cleansing. The law did provide, however, for poor families who could not afford a lamb. They could substitute a bird in the lamb's place. That was what we would be doing that day! We could not afford a lamb for the sacrifice, so we took two turtle doves—one for the sin offering and one to replace the lamb.

We would also dedicate Jesus while we were at the temple. According to our law, every firstborn male child must be dedicated to God—or redeemed at the cost of five shekels sometime after he reached the age of thirty days. The act of dedication or redemption was a reminder that, of all He owned, God claimed only the first fruits. So the child was brought to God and either dedicated or bought back. Either way, he still

---

3. There was a saying, "Those who have never seen Herod's buildings, have never seen beauty." The temple's limestone gleamed like snow in the sunshine.

belonged to God, as do all children. But all who brought their children were forced to remember the One to whom these children really belonged. The parents were also prompted to remember that God spared the firstborn in Egypt and so had a double claim on all firstborn males.[4]

At any rate, here we were—the Messiah, God in human flesh, and his parents coming to His temple with a poor family's offering. I began to doubt once again whether our story was true. Was my baby really the Messiah?

It was shortly after we arrived at the temple that we met old Simeon. He was a man who had been promised by God that he would not die until he had seen the Messiah. It was quite a promise! In waiting for the promise to be fulfilled, poor Simeon had grown quite old and weary of life, and he was ready to die. It was time, he thought. So, in order to have the best chance of seeing the Messiah, he stayed near the temple watching each and every baby boy who was brought in to be dedicated or redeemed.

The day we took my baby to the temple was no different than any other day for old Simeon. He would go up to every mother who was carrying a baby and take a good look at the child. Some of the mothers pulled back from this strange old stooped one, but he insisted on seeing each one. No baby got past him!

Then he saw Jesus, and suddenly this day was different from all the rest! Simeon saw Jesus and, ohhh—such joy!! He could not contain himself. Taking Jesus out of my arms with his withered, trembling hands, he burst into a song that exploded from his body. He danced and laughed and sang, as he swung little Jesus up into the air. I was afraid the tottering old man would drop my child, and I watched with concern.

I did not want to hurt old Simeon's feelings as some of the mothers would have, had old Simeon not been impervious to their actions in his search for the Messiah. At the same time, I wanted to protect my baby. As I stood there on edge, indecisive about what to do, old Simeon suddenly stopped. The dancing was over as quickly as it had begun; the song ended, the laughter gone. Simeon sobered. I could see that he had thought of

---

4. All first fruits, both plant and animal, were to be sacrificed, not as a gift to God, but rather to acknowledge that all fruits are a gift from God. We give God only what already belongs to Him. When it came to children, the first fruits were either dedicated to God, or redeemed for five shekels, as a reminder that all children belong first and foremost to God—often a sobering thought for first time parents. The redeeming was also a reminder that God spared the firstborn in Egypt.

something. Then, looking directly into my heart through the depths of my eyes, he said something about what Jesus was destined to do that I did not understand at the time. The words were spoken with hope, peace, and certainty, but then, with a sadness that had not been there before, he said, "… and a sword will pierce your soul, too." I stood staring at the old man for a moment in disbelief. Then I went numb with a terrible coldness. I felt a steel blade run through my heart—several times—and I knew it would again—sometime in the future. I realized that Simeon knew something that I had suspected all along. Somehow, my son was to suffer terrible things.

There were other "messiahs" in our day. Our people were looking for someone to deliver them from the Romans, and when it became apparent that a young Jewish man was a leader, people would rally behind him, hoping that he was the one. Of course, that meant the possibility of an uprising, a revolt against Rome. That's why Roman officials had begun appointing the High Priests. The priests were in a position to pick out these leaders—these "messiahs"—and they would report them to Rome. Rome would then quickly dispose of them, making an example of them by stripping them of their clothing and crucifying them publicly—disgracing them by their nakedness as they suffered and died. That my son was *the* Messiah was a frightening thought. But he was THE Messiah—God's only begotten, I told myself. Surely it would be different for him. But I knew that Simeon knew, and he was preparing me. "And a sword shall pierce your soul." It did.

Then Anna, the old woman who was a prophetess, came to have a look at Jesus. She was even more frail than Simeon, and I hoped she wouldn't try to hold Jesus and dance around, too. But she seemed content to leave Jesus in my arms. She grinned up at me, a toothless grin that showed her years, and then turning away and pointing her bony, bent finger back toward Jesus, she began praising God and telling all who would listen that my little boy, Jesus, would redeem Israel. She stepped in front of some passers-by, tugged on other's sleeves, and generally did her best to get people to listen to the most important words she had ever spoken. For her this was urgent! She wanted people to know! And people did listen to her—some with mocking grins on their faces, some with looks of sad hope, wishing they dared to believe, still others listened with awe and wonder. Certainly they had prayed for the Messiah. Were they seeing him now? Many of them came near and peered down upon the babe in my arms, who grinned at them in response. As they looked at this seemingly ordinary baby, the expectation and hope on their faces melted into peace and joy. As I watched their faces, the sword left my soul, the horror faded away, and I felt proud and content once again. I knew that God would help me deal with the hard times when they came.

CHAPTER 6

The Magicians

A year passed in Bethlehem. We celebrated Jesus' first birthday, and life settled into a routine. I made friends with other young mothers, and we shared child rearing tips as well as chores. Times were good, and I delighted in mothering my baby boy.

One evening in January, Jesus was sitting on my lap, and I was enjoying rocking him in my arms, playfully trying to coax him to sleep. It was a good night for sleeping. The rainy season had started, and the clouds were gathering, covering the stars and moon that tried in vain to light the dark night. The oil lamp was burning low, and Joseph and I were ready to head for bed, when we noticed that the room seemed strangely brighter! As I looked around, I realized that light was coming in through the north window and was gradually growing stronger as though the source of light were moving in our direction. I could not imagine what it could be. No human could carry a light so bright and move so steadily. Joseph and I had just looked at one another, puzzled, when the light began to leak through the east and west windows as well! The source was obviously overhead, and I began to feel frightened by the lack of a logical explanation for what was happening. Then light began to stream in through the south window and the movement stopped.

Joseph moved closer to me, and we looked at one another again. My heart was beating harder and faster. I sat motionless, no longer rocking the baby. Joseph moved silently to the north window and peered out. A moment later, he looked over his shoulder and whispered, "Some people are coming this way!" As he turned his face back toward the window, I pulled the baby close, and holding him snugly, crept over to Joseph's side. I looked out and saw bobbing lanterns, disclosing the vague forms of people, as they moved in our direction. They obviously were not frightened by the light source, which seemed to have settled directly above the house.

As they came closer, Joseph slipped across the room and covered the sole lamp[1] that had lit our evening activities a few minutes ago. That simple action sent a chill through me for I realized that Joseph was concerned. I snuggled the baby closer and put him to my breast to keep him silent. The little group was drawing near now. I could hear voices, but had trouble making out what was being said. Joseph had returned to my side. He slipped his arm across my shoulder and said quietly, "We'd better get away from the window."

We stooped down, and as we turned and started across the room, one voice came clearly through the window, "The star seems to have stopped over that house! The child must be in there!"

I froze. "The child?" I murmured to myself. "They're looking for my baby?" I held him tighter as tears stung my eyes.

Thoughts raced through my mind. The light over my house was a star? In the cloudy night, a star was lighting up the house? And it had moved there? It made no sense! And why were these people looking for my baby?"

I wanted to believe it was a mistake, but there was Simeon's sword poking at my heart, egging my fears on. What kind of people would have a moving star guiding them? Magicians, perhaps? Men who delved into the spirit world, using the stars and anything else—good or evil—that would seem to lead them to the truth! Magicians were hated by Romans and Jews alike—it was one of the few things we agreed upon. It seemed incredulous that such creatures might have found my child, but it had been an unspoken fear within, that if I harbored God's son, I would meet with the forces of evil who were seeking him in order to do him harm. Magicians[2] dealt in the black arts, but would God allow them to find His son?

Joseph must have seen the look on my face. He was trying to get me to move, and finally he said simply, "It will be all right, Mary! Don't be frightened. Come on! Get out of sight!"

I began to move, but it was too late! There was a loud knock at the door, and Joseph turned to answer the summons. I reached after him.

1. Lamps were covered with a metal basket (peck size) which eventually snuffed the flame. Normally, people went to bed when it got dark, so a lamp was not needed.

2. Although magi often attended kings and heads of state, they were not kings themselves, but merely advisors. Jews had no use for magi because magi tried to predict (control) the future rather than leaving it in God's hands. Elsewhere in the New Testament, magi is translated magician or sorcerer.

"Don't open it!" I begged, pleading with my eyes as well as my whisper.

"We've no real choice," said Joseph gently. "Resisting evil only makes it worse." Then realizing that what he had said was hardly comforting, he glanced back at me. "It's all right," he repeated. "It's probably just some strangers looking for hospitality." His face, although concerned, remained calm and confident.

Joseph cracked the door cautiously, and it was immediately pushed open by some men who, without comment, came into the room—not forcefully, but matter-of-factly, as though they had the right. It was immediately obvious that these men were from another land. We were not unaccustomed to seeing foreigners, but there was something different—something unusual—about them. Then, I realized with horror that these men did indeed carry the marks of magicians! And they were already in our house! There was no chance of hiding or pretending the child was not here. I thought the coming of the shepherds was bad, but that had been nothing compared to this. The men were looking around the room, and of course, they spotted Jesus almost immediately. I sank down into the chair where I had been sitting earlier, and watched these strangers. They carried themselves with certainty, which only frightened me more.

Then one of the group said, "We have come to worship the child who is born to be the King of the Judeans.[3] We saw his star in the East, and traveled to Jerusalem where we expected to find the young king. From Jerusalem the star moved ahead of us, leading us to this house. Is this the child?" There was an air of authority about these men. The light of the lanterns they carried flickered up onto faces that demanded an answer and would tolerate no foolishness. I saw no love of evil in their eyes, but rather a sincerity that revealed a deep desire for truth. I felt some of the tension begin to leave my body, and, realizing how tightly I was holding the baby, I allowed my arms to relax a little. Apparently, these were magicians seeking the truth, wherever it might be found. If it were to be found in evil, so be it, but if it was found in the goodness of a child king, so much the better!

Another of them spoke, "We have long delved into the spirit world, and although Judea is not a significant country, we have come to realize

---

3. The word normally translated *Jews* is in fact a geographical term that refers to the people in the South, or Judea. As explained elsewhere, the people of the South were more trouble to the Romans than the people of the North (Samaritans and Galileans). (The same title used by the magi, King of the Judeans, was later used on the cross.)

that the one who will come to rule the Judeans will rule all spirits as well. If this is the child, he is the ultimate in what we have sought throughout our entire lives. "Is this the child?" The question was repeated. I was vaguely aware that a response was called for on my part, but I continued studying these men, still speechless. I had never been in the company of a magician, but I had heard that there were some who were so involved in the world of demons, that one must stay clear of them for safety's sake. But these men! The things they were saying about my child! He would rule all spirits?! Then all spirits—even evil ones would be obliged to bow at Jesus' command! If that were true, then neither these men nor any other could truly harm my child!

The men were waiting for an answer. "Is this the child?" the question came again, more sternly than before. Still somewhat frightened and taken aback, I managed only to nod my head slightly. Glancing up at Joseph, I saw disapproval in his eyes. He was not sure that we should be revealing our secret to such men as these! But it was too late. I had answered their question.

What happened next was beyond my comprehension. These men came across the room to where I sat holding Jesus, and they knelt at my feet, worshiping Jesus and holding out gifts for my child. I had seen what the presence of Jesus had done to the shepherds, but these were not shepherds! These magicians, although they were outcasts too, were seemingly men of great knowledge, and now they bowed to my son and offered gifts. Expensive gifts, and each one carried meaning that was more precious than its worldly value in riches..

First, was the gift of gold. I had never owned gold! It was the metal of royalty! Was then my son, the Son of God, to be royalty? …a future king?!

"Of course," I whispered, "he is to be a king!"

Next, frankincense was presented as a gift. Frankincense is an incense, a tree resin from Arabia, that was burned by the priests to send sweet smells to God. My son would be a priest? …a holy man?! Yes! I knew that he would! In my excitement and growing joy, I realized that these men recognized far more than I had even considered at this point. But these men were not Jews! Was my son to be a king and priest beyond the borders of our small land? …beyond all borders of all lands?! I knew that when the Messiah came, other nations would come to us! But I had not yet connected that teaching with my son! I looked up at these men with awe.

Then old Simeon's sword pierced through my joy and into my soul as I saw the next gift. It was Myrrh! Myrrh was well known as a pain killer and an ointment for dead bodies!! A chill went through me. Oh, my son! If the other gifts pointed to his life, did this one point to his death? Was my Holy King to suffer as he died?! I was too stunned to acknowledge this last gift!

The pain in my heart passed quickly, though. In the excitement of the moment, there was no time to mull over the words of Simeon or the significance of the gifts. The men were ready to tell their story. They explained how they had known by the stars[4] that the Messiah had been born. They told of their long journey to Jerusalem, and how they had sought out Herod, thinking that the child would have been born into a royal household. It was Herod's advisors who told them that the King would be born in Bethlehem, so they had set out in our direction. As they left Jerusalem, the star that had announced the arrival of the baby began to move along ahead of them, leading them to the house where we lived, and stopping above it. That explained the light. I realized that it was gone now, and that Joseph had uncovered the oil lamp.

When they had finished their story, Joseph asked them more about their visit with Herod. Herod's mother was a Jew, and for the sake of his mother's people, Herod had, among other things, rebuilt the Temple in Jerusalem. He had been a good king for our people in some ways, but there had always been a vicious and cruel side to him, and as he grew older, that side had become more obvious. Herod had arranged for the murder of the only wife he truly loved and had even killed some of his own sons for fear they might try to take his throne.

The magicians admitted that they had told Herod about the baby

---

4. One tradition says that the Magi were followers of Zoroastrianism. Zoroaster was a Persian who studied the stars and rejected the idols of his people saying there was a God who created all things and created them good. He believed evil was evidence that God had enemies and that one must choose between good and evil and cling to the truth. There would be a judgement someday, but salvation could only be attained through the Savior that God would send— a man more righteous than any previous to him, and born of a virgin. When God's people were exiled into Babylon, they were exposed to this teaching, and when Daniel survived the lions' den, King Darius declared that all should worship the God of the Daniel. Thus the magi knew what nation the Messiah would be born into. If this is true, modern day Kurdistan is the land of the magi. At any rate, the main thrust of the birth stories seems to be the involvement of the lowly, the poor, the outcast —in Pastor Schein's words—stench!—and whether the magi were sorcerers who attended a royal court, or foreign followers of a slightly different religion or (quite likely) both, in the Holy Land, they would certainly have fit the category of the outcast.

born to be the King of the Judeans, and that Herod—the current King of the Judeans—had been very interested in knowing exactly when the star had first appeared to them. In fact, they recalled, Herod himself had instructed them to find the child, and then to return to Jerusalem, so that he could know the whereabouts of the infant and come to worship him, too. When I heard that, the skin on my face and scalp tightened, and the hair stood up on my arms as a wave of fear washed over me. These men believed that Herod was sincere, and they were planning to go back and tell him where the baby could be found!

Joseph's eyes met mine. I said nothing. We needed time to think. For now we had guests, and God's Word said that we should provide for foreigners who traveled in our land. We must be faithful to God's Word, as God was always faithful to us. Handing Jesus to Joseph, I went to prepare some food for these travelers.

After the strangers had eaten, we all retired for the night. And a long night it was. I hardly slept at all, wondering and praying about the danger in which we now perceived ourselves to be. It would not be wise to tell our guests what kind of a man Herod was, or try to convince them that they should defy him or be less than truthful with him about what they had found. That would only complicate matters. As I lay thinking what we were to do, I could hear the magicians tossing about. It seemed a restless night for them, as well.

When morning finally came, our foreign friends said that they had been warned in a dream not to go back to Herod. They would be going home by a different route and would be leaving immediately. As I watched them disappear down the road, I pondered all that had happened in the last few hours. My son—a holy King—would draw all the nations together! Then came a thought that was overwhelming—through me, God could work things of life-changing significance!! I was only a poor Jewish girl from an unknown village in an occupied land whose only strength was the God we worshipped. I stood humbled and grateful, my heart swelling with love for this Almighty God who would reach down into the turbulence of this world where so few knew Him—and touch me! I stood gazing into the distance after our departing friends, savoring the feeling of God's love surrounding and strengthening me. Such days as this were precious to me, because on days when I doubted, I could look back, remember, and be reassured that God's love is there even when we do not feel it! God's love of us never changes! God always gives us what we need!

When the magicians were finally out of sight, I turned to Joseph. "What are we to do?" I asked. I was fully aware of the immediate danger that we faced, but for the time, my fear had subsided. God's peace and strength had enveloped me. There was no panic.

"We will wait for God's instructions," he said simply. "God will show us what we must do to protect Jesus." This he said, still gazing down the road. Then, turning to me and looking into my eyes thoughtfully, he continued. "God will lead us. But it will not be easy. I … I wish you didn't have to go through all this. I love you so, and I would like …" Then brightening just a little, "When you told God you would be his slave, you let us in for a terrifying, exciting life that is to be filled with sorrow and joy. It's a life that is going to require self-discipline and trust and doing things we don't want to do, but …" His eyes filled with wonder and became moist. "Think what we're a part of! Can you believe what wonders God is working through ordinary people like us?" Joseph's eyes drifted back to the road, and he slipped his arm around me. We stood there together, quietly absorbing the moment, until we heard the baby cry. He was awake and needed attention. God's wonders would have to be worked in the midst of diapers and milk.

Going inside, I found the child sadly in need of care. I proceeded with my task, cleaning and feeding him, reflecting that even such things as this are an integral part of doing God's will. I continued wondering where God's will would take us next. Only yesterday I was comfortably going about tasks such as this one, for the moment forgetting who this child was. Now I had been reminded of his identity, and had learned that he was in great danger. With or without the help of the magi, Herod would have no trouble finding us. There were the shepherds and all whom they had told, and besides, Bethlehem was a small city,[5] having only about 1000 residents.

Throughout the day, Joseph and I talked occasionally about the situation, but neither of us was sure what we should do. We knew that God would lead us, and we must wait, but it is sometimes difficult to wait for his leading.

---

5. By definition, in Bible times, a settlement was a city if it was surrounded by a wall. The title, city, had nothing to do with size.

That night Joseph had a dream that directed us. We were to flee at once to Egypt.

CHAPTER 7

Egypt

It was a frightening thing picking up and leaving hurriedly in the middle of the night. Concern for my son's life was enough to drive me to do anything, but I had never been out at night for any length of time, and I was afraid. It was at night that the spirits roamed, looking for bodies to inhabit—people to possess. Later in his life, my son would cast out such spirits, but for now, like all people of our day, I feared those spirits, so I was edgy as well as being frightened for my son's life. At least the clouds that hung in the sky, releasing the lightly falling rain, would cover the moon. The spirits loved the moonlight and were most active when it was shining brightly.

The gathering of the essentials we would carry with us on our trip was accomplished quickly. Joseph and I exchanged a questioning look, searching one another's eyes for any doubt that we were doing the right thing, and finding none, we picked up our loads and headed for the door. Joseph stopped. Finding my eyes again, he whispered, "If Herod's men are near, the baby might be safer in my arms." I nodded, knowing he was right. The Romans would strike down either of us to get the baby, and Joseph, being taller and stronger than I, had a better chance, so I quickly relinquished the child to his arms. I picked up Joseph's load, and we slipped out into the cold, wet, night. We moved quickly away from the house, our eyes adjusting to the darkness. Every movement in the shadows caught my attention and sent chills racing through me! Spirits ... Herod's henchmen ... Anything could be hiding, waiting there.

Leaving Bethlehem as quietly and quickly as possible, we headed south toward Hebron, where we would hit the trade route and follow it west to Gaza and on to Egypt. As the city walls fell into the distance behind us, I felt some small relief. At least Herod would not find us in Bethlehem!

Jesus had accommodatingly slept as we had begun our flight, but after a few miles, he began fretting a little and nuzzling at Joseph. Sensing the urgency in his parents as he awoke, the child wanted the comfort of his mother's warm milk. We stopped long enough to exchange loads again, and then resumed our rapid pace even before I got the child nestled up to my breast. I could get him into position, and he could nurse[1] easily enough as we continued to put distance between us and Bethlehem. The gentle rain kept the road wet, and the stones that comprised that road, worn smooth by the feet of centuries of travelers, were slippery. I shielded Jesus from the wetness as well as I could in the midst of slipping, sliding, and nearly falling a few times. It was a relief when the sun rose and the rain ceased, even though I knew we would not stop walking until evening came.

At daybreak we were joined by other travelers. No longer alone, we had to consciously slow ourselves lest the growing fear within should drive us at a pace that would signal to others that we were fleeing. It was that same fear that strengthened us beyond our normal capabilities and kept us going in spite of our weariness. When we had first begun our flight, it seemed important only to get away from Bethlehem, but as we had walked during the night, there had been time to think about the man we were fleeing. Herod was a cruel, sly man who did not think reasonably and did not like being foiled. He had eyes and ears everywhere in his kingdom. We could easily be seized and our baby killed at any time. No one must know the reason for our journey or even sense that we were frightened. We must discipline ourselves in order to accomplish God's will.

Jesus endured the trip well. As for me—well, it's amazing how heavy a young child can become when you walk and carry him all night and all day. My strength and stamina were high from many years of carrying jars of water from the well. Jesus weighed less than a jar of water, but I could not carry him on my head as I did the water, and bearing his weight unevenly for so long made my back and arms ache. Joseph helped, but it was merely a matter of trading loads, since he had his share of things to carry, too.

I was exhausted by the time evening came, and we finally stopped to rest. Even so, my sleep was fitful with worry. The full import of things would not leave me. If I mishandled this situation, the child would die

---

1. Babies were weaned around the age of three.

without ever doing what he was sent to do. I wanted to do a good job as the mother of God's son, and the present danger weighed heavily upon me. Beyond that was the fact that this was my baby boy, and I loved him as any mother loves her baby. I could not bear the thought of something happening to him. So, when that second night passed, it was with relief that I saw the light of dawn! I was still tired, but now we could move on in the safety of daylight.

As we walked along on the second day, I remembered Joseph of old—Jacob's favored son—slave—ruler of Egypt—Dreamer!! Once we passed Gaza we would walk the same roads that he had walked—perhaps the same dust would powder our feet that had once powdered his! He had not gone to Egypt by choice either, but through his going and his faithfulness to God, much good was accomplished—many lives were saved.

Joseph's people had stayed too long in Egypt. Our land, the promised land, was a land that flowed with milk and honey only because God sent the rains in due time,[2] the life giving morning dew in the dry season, and the cooling breeze each day. Living in our land had always strengthened our faith, because we were forced to depend upon God—to acknowledge that He was in control. In Egypt our ancestors had the luxury of irrigation and consequently felt in control of their own lives. Hence, they succumbed to the temptation to stay put, where crops grew with ease, wealth abounded, and life seemed easier. As a result of their desire to control their own destinies, they became enslaved by the Egyptians and remained slaves until God took control, and, by his mighty hand, led them home. Joseph and I must learn from the stories of old, and not be tempted to stay in Egypt as our ancestors had, for Jesus was God's son and must live among God's people, working His will. Remembering the sword of Simeon made Egypt a real temptation. Perhaps I could save my child—and myself—a lot of pain. but the story of our patriarch Joseph was a good reminder to look beyond immediate gratification to the long term effects of our decisions. We must discipline ourselves to trust only God and to follow only God's will.

Thinking of those stories of old and pondering the truths contained

---

2. If the rains did not come or did not come at the right time, there would be famine in the land. In November the heavy rains came, breaking up the land that had been baked hard during the dry season. The crops were planted around December. The gentler, light rain came in January and ended in March. If the hard rain came during this time, it would destroy the crops. The rains had to come in "due time."

in them, helped me carry the child without dwelling on my weariness. Time passed in a blur, and a tiring and trying ten days later, we arrived safely in Egypt. We settled in quickly. Joseph found a demand for his trade and was able to pick up enough work to sustain us. We located a place to live and tended to the necessities of life.

We had been in Egypt only about three months when Joseph woke me one dark night. "Mary!" He touched my shoulder. I started, still jumpy from all that had happened, but Joseph quickly reassured me. "It's all right, Mary. An angel came to me in a dream and told me that I should take you and Jesus home. Herod is dead! Those who wanted to kill Jesus are gone! We're safe!" Joseph gave me a hug. "We'll leave right away in the morning. I'm between jobs. There's nothing to keep us here." He took a deep breath and hugged me again. "We can be back in Bethlehem in no time. I'll just pick up where I left off. I had some business built up. I'm sure I can still get some of the jobs I had contracted for. Oh, Mary, it will be so good to be back in our ancestral home!" He was giving me another hug when the baby stirred and began to make little grunting sounds, trying to get himself awake.

"Shhhh," I whispered. "Don't wake the baby!" With the long journey ahead, we both knew he needed a good night's rest. We lay back down and Jesus drifted back into a peaceful sleep. I poked Joseph. "You just don't want to go back to Nazareth and explain Jesus' birthday coming too soon!" I teased. I was happy to be going home.

Joseph chuckled. "Go to sleep," he said.

The next morning, we gathered our scant belongings and set out early. When the sun grew high in the sky, we stopped to rest and eat. There was no rush on this journey, but we were both so excited, we found ourselves eating quickly, eager to be on our way. Before we continued our journey, we went to the well to get some water and Joseph heard someone talking about Bethlehem. He stopped and listened. Jesus was fussing in my ear, so I wasn't sure what Joseph had heard. After a moment, he turned to me. "Stay here," he said. "I'll be right back." He approached the men who were talking about our hometown and introduced himself. I watched from a distance as Joseph exchanged serious words with the men, and shaking his head, turned and came back to me.

"Change of plans," he said with a look of concern on his face. "Things are not as simple as I thought they would be." He was silent, his eyes searching as his mind looked for an answer.

"What is it, Joseph?" I asked quietly, hoping nothing would spoil the light hearted mood of our journey.

His eyes came back to me. "I'm sorry, Mary," he said. "It's not that bad. It's just that I had my heart set on Bethlehem, but ... Mary, Archeleus has taken his father Herod's place in ruling over Judea. He is even more wicked than his father was! I'm afraid to live under him! These men say he killed 3000 of the most prominent people in Judea, just to show people that he is like his father—only more ruthless. Considering he was raised by a man who killed his first wife, his mother-in-law, three of his own sons, and all the Sanhedrin, no one should be surprised, I guess." Joseph studied his feet. Little puffs of dust arose as he moved his sandals, still thinking.

"What are we to do?" I asked, watching Joseph's face. Your angel said we must return to our home,"

"We do have some choices," Joseph replied. "It seems that the old fox Herod didn't leave the whole kingdom to Archeleus. He divided it up, putting various sons in charge of various areas."

"What about Nazareth?" I asked. "Is it safe to go there?" I thought to myself that I would like to see my mother again and introduce her to my baby.

"Nazareth might not be much better," Joseph was saying hesitantly. His eyes found my face. "Antiochus is ruling the Galilee. He's also known for his cruelty."

I looked at Joseph. His concern was obviously growing. "God told you we should go back," I said. "The only question is where." I thought for a moment. "You know, I've heard that most of the time Antiochus is too wrapped up in the little petty things of life to pay much attention to what's going on around him. I can't imagine that a man whose first priority is parties would ever pay any attention to Nazareth! It's too poor and out of the way to be of much interest to him."

Joseph thought about these things for a while. Finally he said, "I think you're right. Let's head for Nazareth."

The news about the current rulers put a bit of a damper on our trip, but it was still good to be going home. Life would never be simple as long as Rome ruled. We knew that.

It took us a couple of weeks to get back to Nazareth, but once we were there and saw the old familiar house that we had left nearly a year and a half before, we were sure we had made the right decision. It was so good to see family and friends again. Mother was beside herself with joy over her grandson and delighted in the prospect of caring for him occasionally. Joseph resumed work in his old carpentry shop, and life was good.

One day while I was drawing water at the well, another young mother said, "So, Mary, what do you know about all those babies who were killed in Bethlehem?"

I was stunned. I had no idea what she was talking about, but I felt the hair stand up on the back of my neck. "Why, nothing," I said. "What do you mean?"

"Well, you were in Bethlehem, weren't you?" She seemed surprised. "I guess Herod got it into his head that a baby had been born who was going to unseat him as king, so he sent his troops to Bethlehem with orders to kill all the baby boys under two years of age. Fifteen[3] died in all, they say. I'm surprised Jesus wasn't one of them! How did you manage to hide him?"

I stood in shocked silence as old Simeon's sword pierced my soul again. The woman was waiting for an answer. "Uhm… we… " My throat grew thick and ached as I fought back tears. "We made a trip to Egypt. It … uhm… " I swallowed hard. "… must have happened while we were there," I managed to respond.

"Good thing you were gone," she replied. Sensing my distress, she continued "Sorry, I didn't mean to upset you."

"It's all right. I… I just didn't know!" I said.

She looked at me sadly, and I turned and started for home. I had no idea! What would she say if she knew that all those babies had died in place of my son? They were dead, and my son lived! If I had stayed, I would be the only mother in Bethlehem grieving the loss of a son. As it was, fifteen other mothers, all of whom I surely knew, were grieving in my stead. I could just see them clinging to their babies as the soldiers ripped them away and killed them, or maybe just killed them right there in their mothers' arms. I had lived the death of my child many times in my mind, but for these mothers it was real—not just a fear—not just a dream… I was so sorry…

---

3. With a population of only about 1000 and considering the infant mortality rate of that time, fifteen is probably the maximum number that could have died.

CHAPTER 8

Jesus is 12

I never forgot the mothers who had lost their babies in Bethlehem. They had made a great sacrifice while my baby lived on in order that God's plan might be accomplished. Those mothers did not know why their babies had died. They only knew that they were dead. What grief they must have endured! They were in my prayers, but even as I prayed, my life went on. Like all people, I had a job to do.

Joseph and I settled into a routine in Nazareth. We delighted in our son, and devoted ourselves to rearing him properly. We believed it was important that he be involved in all of the religious festivals of our faith, so each year we tried to go to Jerusalem for the Passover celebration. Some years we were able to go, and some years we were not, but the year that Jesus was twelve, I was determined that we would go. It would be Jesus' last year as a child, and I wanted to enjoy the festivities one more time with him at my side.[1]

The trip that year started out as usual with our friends in Nazareth seeing us off with regrets that they could not join us. Passover comes at the beginning of the grain harvests,[2] and it was a rare year when the northern people could make the three-day trip down to the temple for the week-long celebration. We were fortunate. Joseph, being a carpenter, could get away. Nazareth was a small village, and Joseph knew the needs of each farmer well. He had for years kept them in farm implements, which he both made and repaired. So, before we left, he made sure there were plenty of spare tools available. If a farmer had problems, he would not be left

---

1. Once boys reached the age of thirteen, they became adults and joined the men in making the sacrifice in the temple, instead of staying outside with the women.

2. Since God's people had long been an agricultural community, the festivals had both agricultural and religious significance. Hence, Passover is the celebration of the barley harvest and the deliverance from Egypt, Pentecost (fifty days after Passover) is wheat harvest and the giving of the Torah, etc. Few northerners could be gone for thirteen days (six days of travel, seven days of Passover) at the beginning of the grain harvests.

wanting in our absence. Joseph had met his obligations, and we set out on what was going to be a big adventure—bigger than we suspected as we left Nazareth in high spirits that day.

As we started out, I could not help but think how different this trip was from the one we had made to Bethlehem the year Jesus was born. What a difficult time that had been! I was terribly uncomfortable with my pregnancy and frightened about the possibility of delivering my child among strangers. We had trudged down these same roads, and those old feelings of uncertainty and fear filled me once again. I indulged myself for a time, reliving the past, but then I put all sadness aside and turned my eyes on Jesus. All the fear, worry, and exertion that I had been through had paid off, and I was looking forward to traveling with him this year. It was fun talking with him and watching him interact with the other young people. I found such delight in him, and I'm afraid I was becoming a little smug about being the mother of such a fine young man. He was indeed someone to be proud of! Jesus seemed so grown up now. He was everything that a son should be.

Looking at him as we walked along, my heart filled with love and joy. My throat swelled and tears threatened as I thought about what a blessing he had been to us! Joseph and I had watched him grow and do all the things that other boys do—going to school at the synagogue, learning his father's trade, and being taught the usual things that mothers teach in the home—manners, proper speech, how to treat others and how to take care of himself. He had been an easy child to raise, and I had many precious memories. As I walked along the road watching my son, I remembered comforting him over the skinned knees he had gotten from playing too hard with the other children. Happy memories of him as a child, needing his mother, caused my mind to slide from one past event to another.

I relived taking him to the Sea of Galilee and watching him wade into that crystal blue water to splash and play. Once again, I saw him swim for the first time and felt him on my lap as he fell asleep listening to Joseph tell the stories of old. I watched as he proudly read to me for the first time, and I heard his child's voice praying prayers that marked him as one of God's people. So much goes into raising a child, and there is nothing like the joy and pride of watching that child grow and become what God has created him or her to be.

My reverie did not continue for long that first day. Trips such as these were community events. People always traveled in groups for safety's sake, so this was a time not only to be together as a family, free from the cares of daily tasks, but also a time to visit with old friends and to make new ones. Soon someone called my name.

"Mary, is that you?" I immediately recognized Naomi[3] from Sephoris. We had played together as children, and I had missed her a great deal when my family had moved away. We embraced and began immediately to catch up on all that we had missed. It was so good to see her! She was married, too, and she pointed out her children in the crowd. I pointed out Jesus as mine, and she was immediately taken with him. "Oh, do you think he'll be a rabbi, Mary? I always thought that if you had a son, he would become a rabbi, since your faith is so deep." I smiled at her, and we walked together in silence for a time.

Shortly we noticed a group pulling close together. "Oh, Naomi, the story telling has begun!" I said. "Let's go listen!" As children, we had loved this custom of our people and had learned so much from it! It was one of the ways that our heritage was passed on to the younger generation.

On journeys like this one, or even when just a small group was out walking, someone would point out the places where the events of old had happened, and then tell the story. It was such fun, and it occupied much of our time on the road, keeping our minds off our weariness and the distance that lay ahead. There was such a great variety of stories to tell! Our little land[4] was so rich in the history of our people that event was piled on top of event. If there was one story to tell of a particular place along the way, there were probably at least two or three more. As we neared Mount Tabor, we heard the story of God using rain to bog down the enemy in mud and deliver them into the hands of Barak and Deborah. A little further, at Arbela, we heard that this was the sight where Gideon and a handful of men had won a battle, showing God's power working through them.

Then we neared Shunem, and Jesus took a turn, telling the story of the woman whose only son died and was restored to life by Elisha. The youngsters in the group sometimes took a turn at storytelling on such journeys. It was a time for them to practice, and the rest of us could see

3. Naomi is a fictional character. Tradition says Mary was born in Sephoris and later moved to Nazareth with her parents. People from Nazareth and Sephoris would have traveled the same route to Jerusalem.
4. The entire land is smaller than Indiana, about 100 miles long and forty miles wide.

which ones might become storytellers[5] when they were older. But when Jesus took a turn, he told the story as though he were one of the seasoned storytellers. He offered insights such as came only from the best of them. He told the story of the woman of Shunem, and later other stories, with such meaning and in such wondrous detail that they came alive. Everyone who listened to Jesus experienced the story just as our ancestors must have. He spoke with great authority in his voice, though he was still a child. Many of the people tearfully thanked Jesus afterward, and even came to me to tell me what a good job he had done, and how much it meant to them. I nearly burst with pride. No doubt, we had done a fine job of teaching our son. I could not take credit for the way in which he retold the stories we had taught him. That was a natural talent... but then, he was our son. Little did I know that on this trip, I would be taught once again whose son this really was.

The group was in good spirits and still having a fine time when we reached Jerusalem three days later. We all agreed that we would meet at the Temple Mount after Passover and make our return trip together. Then each family went its own way, some staying with relatives or friends in Jerusalem, others setting up tents outside the city walls, where they would camp during the holiday.

Joseph, Jesus and I went on west into the Sorek Valley to Ein Kerem where we stayed with Zachariah, Elizabeth, and their son John.[6] It was not far from Jerusalem, maybe five or six miles.

The city was overrun with Passover visitors; the population nearly tripled. We were lucky to have relatives outside the city to put us up, even though it meant walking a little farther.

As we neared Zachariah's home, we heard a familiar voice, "Jesus! You're here! Put your things down. Have I got something to show you!"

"John!" cried Jesus. The boys ran toward each other. John grabbed hold of the bundle that Jesus was carrying, and together they ran by the house, depositing the load at the doorway and taking off toward the spring around which this small village was built. Both boys had always

---

5. Since books (scrolls copied by hand) were rare, people with talent were chosen to memorize the stories and pass them on.

6. The Holy Family may very well have stayed with Elizabeth and Zachariah when they went to Jerusalem, since they were relatives, and Mary and Elizabeth shared the knowledge that their sons were born for special reasons. During Passover, anyone who had a relative nearby stayed with them, due to the crowding in the city, and five or six miles was nearby for people who were used to walking everywhere they went.

had a fascination with the cool, cleansing, living[7] water that bubbled out of the rock, giving life to this otherwise desert valley. Joseph and I stopped and laughed as we watched the boys run off. It was a joy to see them together.

John and Jesus were nearly the same age—John was six months older—and they had always enjoyed being together at Passover. I used to look at them and marvel that they could enjoy one another so much—they were so different!

John's parents had taken a Nazarite vow at his birth, so his hair had never been cut, and he did not drink wine or other strong beverages, even when we celebrated the Passover meal. But the difference between the boys went far beyond that. Perhaps it was the difference between Jesus' being raised in the North and John in the South. People who lived in the North—in Galilee—where things were greener and life a bit softer, tended to be a gentler, more relaxed people. The south was harsher. It was rocky and dry; more of a desert. There people had to depend entirely upon God for life. It was God who sent or withheld the rains in season and sent the refreshing dew each morning of the dry months. It was God who brought the cooling, life-giving breeze from the west off the Mediterranean, or the hot, deadly shrov[8] from the barren wasteland to the east. Because the Southerners were so dependent on God's actions, they were very zealous in their faith, and the zealousness extended to all areas of their lives. For them, there was no compromising and no overlooking shortcomings, because an indiscretion might mean the "Judgement of God" coming and causing famine. Consequently, even though John and Jesus shared the same faith, John was a zealot[9] in all that he did, while Jesus was gentler and more relaxed about life in general.

---

7. Spring water was called "living water," distinguishing it from cistern water. (The "wells" in the Bible were actually deep pits in the limestone that caught rain water. To us they would be considered cisterns.) The village was Ein Kerem meaning Spring of Vineyard, since the spring (ein) provided for an extraordinary vineyard (Kerem). Other vineyards depended on dew in the dry season; at Ein Kerem, a spring provided moisture.

8. When the wind shifted and came off the desert instead of the Mediterranean, it was dry and hot, reaching temperatures of 130 degrees. This wind or "shrov" dehydrated plants and animals, destroying all life, and sometimes creating famine in the land. A shrov called "the Judgement of God," could kill an unprotected human being in fifteen minutes or less, and was said to make people do crazy things (e.g. Bathsheba taking a bath on the roof where she could be seen by King David).

9. The "zealots" mentioned in the Gospels were from the South. Judas was the only zealot or Southerner among the disciples.

The difference in the boys showed in their activities together. John played strictly by the rules, while Jesus was more flexible, almost casual about keeping the rules in the games they played—which was nearly more than John could bear. He would keep the rules down to the last letter. Jesus definitely knew a freedom in his life that John did not. Yet when the two of them talked religion, there was unity in spite of their differences. John seemed to recognize something in Jesus—even then—that he respected and made way for.

I marveled at seeing them together. How I loved them both! Memories, both painful and peaceful, flooded back each time I witnessed the wisdom of these two youth; memories of being an unwed pregnant teen, visiting Elizabeth and seeing her grow heavy with John, Joseph's rejection and then acceptance of my pregnancy, the birth in Bethlehem, and Simeon's sword. Oh, Simeon's sword! It struck pangs in my heart each time I heard these two discuss their faith. They were both set apart for God's work, and one could not say what pain that might bring to them.

When Zachariah and Joseph relaxed and talked, Jesus and John would often sit and listen. Elizabeth and I listened, too, as we served the meals and tended to household chores.[10] Elizabeth, being from a priestly family, was more interested in the talk of the temple than most women. I, too was interested, and Zachariah seemed to appreciate all of us as an audience.

He was distressed with some of the customs at the temple, and there were few people with whom he was comfortable sharing his views. So when we came to visit, he talked. He talked of the money changers, who worked at tables in the temple exchanging "temple money" for the Roman coins[11] that people brought for their offerings. The money changers had originally been put in place as a convenience for the people, and it was a good idea in the beginning. But, as with so many good ideas, this one had gone awry. The money changers began charging more and more for the temple money, so it was costing the people a great deal to bring

10. Women did not sit and eat with the men, but served them and then ate separately. Women who were interested in the conversation of the men occasionally sat at the back of the room when they were finished serving and listened, but household chores came first, and the women did not participate in the conversation—only listened. (Consider Mary and Martha, Luke 10:38-42.)

11. Roman money could not be allowed in the temple since it bore the image of the Roman ruler and the commandment forbade images.

offerings to God, and the money changers were getting rich as a result! Zachariah lamented long and loudly over the immorality of taking advantage of people in such a way.

Zachariah talked of the temple lambs, which, in his eyes, were no different than the temple money. Originally, lambs had been provided at the temple for families who had to come a long distance to worship and found it difficult to arrive with their perfect lambs intact. Lambs that had been injured or blemished along the way were disqualified as sacrificial lambs, so it was a nice gesture in the beginning. But again, there was the potential for wealth at the expense of those who came to worship. Consequently, according to some reports, the priests became much stricter when examining lambs that families brought from their own flocks and, more often than not, the families would be required to exchange their "blemished" lamb for a temple lamb—at a price, of course. Zachariah had good reason to believe that many of the rejected lambs were later sold to other families as being perfect!

Zachariah also talked about the doves. Doves were brought as sacrifices by those who could not afford a lamb—by the poor. Again, the temple officials were making a considerable amount of money, this time by selling doves at rates that exploited the poor who only wanted to worship God! It was not right!

Jesus and John paid attention to Zachariah's words, and then had lengthy discussions of their own. They discussed the rituals, which had been devised as a way of helping people approach the unapproachable God safely, but now were actually keeping people away from God. It appeared as though both people and God were being used to make a few rich in the name of religion. Such serious talk it was for boys who should be enjoying their holiday! Both were destined for times that would cause Simeon's sword to pierce my soul, and I longed for them to enjoy the time at hand.

Our week-long Passover celebration was filled with conversation, worship and feasting, relaxing and the enjoyment of being together. The week went by too quickly, and soon it was time to return to Nazareth. At the appointed time, we reluctantly went into Jerusalem to meet our caravan near the Temple Mount. As we walked along the road toward the city, I thought about the week's events. Jesus had continued to prove to be an exceptional boy. Next year he would become a man. After his thirteenth birthday, he would go before the sages for blessing, admonition, and encouragement. Then he would assume his place as an adult in matters of religion. For legal matters, he would have to wait until he was 20, but as one of God's people, he would be an adult long before I was ready to let go.

I had no reason to dread Jesus' becoming an adult. I had done a good job and was confident that he would be a fine man. Certainly, no one could fault my mothering.

Perhaps if other mothers had raised their sons the way I had raised mine, well … But then Jesus was definitely a cut above the others when it came to matters pertaining to God—and what else mattered? I felt a little condescending toward other mothers—but after all, I had been chosen to mother the Messiah. There must have been a reason. My foolish pride would soon be cut to the quick.

In the end, I would come to believe that I was chosen not because of my marvelous mothering ability, but because of my willingness to be obedient and endure tremendous emotional pain whenever it was necessary in order for God's plan to be fulfilled.

The caravan gathered and had not even left Jerusalem when we were caught up in the storytelling once again. One person told the story of the Garden of Eden, pointing to the Temple Mount—the traditional center of the garden. Someone else spoke of Noah's ark landing on what was now the altar rock. Another picked up the story with Abraham taking Isaac to the same spot to sacrifice him. This continued as we crossed the Kidron and climbed up the Mount of Olives. The site of Nob at the top invited the story of Goliath's sword, presented to God by David, and kept there by the priest, Ahimelech, until David reclaimed it. Of course, Jericho brought the story of Joshua and the battle and the marching that brought down the walls. Then as we neared the Jordan River, there was the site where Joshua led the people across the river into the beginning of a new life for the people of our nation. Little did I know that some day, my Jesus—whose name in Hebrew is Joshua—would be baptized there as he began the journey that would result in new life for people of all nations.

As we reached the Jordan and headed north, groups of people were gathering around different storytellers to hear favorite stories of the places we passed. "Over there," someone said, "the jeering youth were mauled by the bear when Elijah cursed them."

"From that spot, Elijah was lifted into heaven by a whirlwind."

I was sure that Jesus was in the middle of one of the groups. I longed to get close enough to hear his exceptional talent, but I could not see which group he was in. Oh well! I was content to let others profit from his insight. It was enough to know that I was his mother.

When we stopped for the night, we looked for Jesus to join us. I built a fire and cooked our bread on hot stones, but as I worked, I had that nagging feeling deep inside, that Jesus was not going to show up. I had not seen him all day!

When the pancake-like bread was ready, and Jesus still had not appeared, we began to search for him. We had many relatives and friends in the group, and I prayed that he was with one of them. As we went from family to family and saw one after another shake their heads, my fear grew until it nearly consumed me. I could hardly breathe when the last family confirmed what the others had said; they had not seen Jesus since that morning at the Temple mount. The tears flowed freely now as I looked up at Joseph, hoping he would have an answer. His head shook just slightly as his saddened eyes met mine. There was no other place to look for our son. It was evident that we must return to Jerusalem.

We could not leave until morning. The path from Jericho up to Jerusalem passed through ravines and gorges where all kinds of things hid, snakes, mountain lions, and ne'er-do-wells who would as soon take your life as your purse. It was not safe for lone travelers in the daytime. We could not possibly travel that road at night.

There was no need for tents or coverings of any kind that night, since there is little dew on the West Bank, so we simply lay down when the rest of our group went to bed.

Wearied from the long walk, we slept, but even in the midst of merciful sleep, our worry about Jesus kept us from resting.

What had happened to our son? He was such a good boy. He would not have deliberately stayed behind, giving us such grief. Something terrible must have happened to him. Perhaps he had offended a Roman soldier, or maybe one of our own zealots had latched on to him for some reason. Surely someone had seen something. He was with the group at the Temple Mount. Could someone have abducted him right in the midst of the crowd? What terrible things might he be suffering even as we lay resting? Oh, if only God would deliver him back into our hands …

My eyes opened many times to find the stars shining that night, and it was such a relief when at last I saw the dim light of predawn in the sky. The rising sun[12] was always a sign that God was still in his heaven and still in control, and the lifting shadows told me we would soon see the sun. As I sat up, I sensed Joseph doing the same. I turned and looked at him through swollen, burning eyes. My head throbbed with worry and my muscles ached with fatigue. I could see that Joseph was in no better shape than I was, and without speaking, we got up and began to prepare for our journey back to Jerusalem. There was bread left from supper—we had not felt much like eating—and that would do for breakfast, along with a few raisins which I had carried with us. We agreed to eat as we walked so that we could get started immediately. Others of our group were rousing as we left camp, and they wished us well. Naomi gave me a hug and looked at me unhappily. We had hoped for another trip together, and she shared my concern for my son. Saying goodbye, we left the camp.

The sun was well up when we reached the road from Jericho to Jerusalem. We fell in with some other people who were making the same trip. My thoughts raced as we moved along. Where was Jesus now? I tried to recite Psalms in my mind. It was better that I pray to God in the words He had given us to pray than to let my mind wander and worry. Surely, God would keep our son safe.

It was mid afternoon when we reached Jerusalem. We looked around the Temple Mount briefly, not really expecting to see Jesus, but hoping nonetheless. Not seeing him anywhere, we headed for Ein Kerem to see if Jesus had gone back to Zachariah's. When we arrived and realized he was not there either, our last vestige of hope left us. It was growing dark now. Elizabeth and Zachariah spoke words of comfort, and John, with all the maturity of a serious twelve-year-old, assured us that Jesus was quite capable of taking care of himself. He was sure we would find him safe and sound. All three made us feel welcome as they encouraged us to eat and rest. We could begin a search in earnest at first light in the morning.

It was another restless night. I imagined all sorts of things happening to Jesus. Perhaps he had realized too late that the caravan had left. Then he had gone down that treacherous road toward Jericho and fallen prey to those who lurk there waiting for lone travelers. Perhaps they had beaten him when they found he had little money and had thrown him in

---

12. When the sun rose, it was always a sign to God's people that God was still in control. So important was this sign that, even today, East is at the top of maps from that part of the world.

the ditch where he lay suffering, waiting for me to find him. What if I had walked right past him and failed to see him lying there—and he had seen me but had been unable to cry out. I had looked for him as we hurried along, but maybe I had missed seeing him.

I dozed off for a while, then awoke, my mind still working. Maybe robbers had carried Jesus off and were having fun at his expense—taunting and hurting him, forcing him to do things he didn't want to do—even trying to make a robber of him.

Maybe he was in a Roman prison for having crossed a soldier or broken some law, or maybe he was just someone the soldiers decided to make an example of. Everyone knew that no one who was arrested by the Romans would make it to a cell without being beaten and bloodied—broken noses were commonplace in Roman arrests. If only I could get to him to comfort him.

What if a group of zealots had grabbed him, and was even now trying to indoctrinate him? Jesus would never go along with their violent ways.

I worried all through the night, blaming myself. If only I had been more watchful. Maybe I had expected too much of him. He seemed so grown up, but he was, after all, only twelve. If only God would deliver him and give me another chance ... I would do better somehow.

Finally, after a night that lasted much too long, dawn came. We were up and on our way as soon as we could get out of the house. Zachariah, Elizabeth, and John set out to help. We divided the names of people we knew to whom Jesus might possibly have gone if he had he simply missed the caravan. Then we split up so that we could cover more territory. Old Zachariah and Elizabeth would cover the homes in Ein Kerem, just in case Jesus had gone to one of them. Joseph and I headed back into Jerusalem to check with people there. Young John went to the few other people Jesus knew in the area. He was swift of foot and took off running at once. He would return quickly and check with each of us to see if we had found Jesus and then carry messages between us. If we found Jesus, we would send word to the others.

We began the day with new hope. Zachariah's family was being so helpful, it lifted our spirits, but it didn't take long for that new hope to dwindle. At each house we heard the same words. No, no one had seen him. Often I felt the disapproval in their voices. How could we possibly lose a son! What kind of boy was he, and what kind of parents were we?! It hurt to feel their judgement, but as we continued our search, I cared less and less what people thought. I just longed to see my son.

It was still early morning when the list of friends was exhausted and we set to wandering the streets of Jerusalem, asking anyone with an ear, if they had seen our son. They would recognize him by the light color of his northern clothing[13] and his Galilean accent, we explained. The streets of Jerusalem were narrow and dark, making a maze among tall buildings. Merchants were putting out their wares as we wandered around, hoping for a sight of Jesus. The tables of breads and other foods and trinkets had no lure for us this morning. We were desperate in our search for our son and could only long for him and nothing else. As we asked various merchants if they might have seen him, one food vendor said a boy of about that age had done some work for him in return for food the day before, and then had headed in the direction of the temple. I was afraid to hope. If it was Jesus, and he was not being held by the zealots or the Roman soldiers, what was he doing?

Joseph and I looked at one another, puzzled, and then headed for the temple. Joseph stopped to ask one of the temple guards if he had seen a boy of Jesus' description. "Yes," he said. "The boy is in the temple even now."

My throat tightened and ached, and I could not speak. Joseph put his arm around me and steered me into the temple. There, sitting among the teachers, was Jesus! He did not see us come in, since both he and the teachers were so engrossed in the questions and answers they were trading. Never had teachers been so caught up by listening to a child.

Both his questions and answers had evidently caught them off guard. I, however, was not impressed! A flood of emotions filled me. At first I felt relief to find my son unharmed, then utter disbelief that both he and the teachers sat here, completely engrossed in their own worlds, while anxious parents scoured the city looking for their missing son, imagining the worst.

Then I became angry. How could this son of whom I was so proud and in whom I took such delight be so oblivious to my feelings?! By now, tears were streaming down my cheeks.

---

13. People in the North wore white—people in the South wore black. The colors changed slowly inbetween.

"Child!" I burst out—reminding him that he was not a man yet—not until next year—and that he was still under my authority until then. There was a shocked silence among the teachers as they jerked their heads toward me. I had jolted them out of their deep, important thoughts. Good! I was making an impression! Even Joseph's jaw dropped as he automatically let go of my arm and moved back a step, separating himself from my attack. Only Jesus seemed unaffected by my outburst, and that only drove my anger deeper. "How is it that you treat your parents?" I asked, trying to twist a little guilt out of him. "Have we been negligent parents that you would now be a negligent son, sitting here talking while our hearts are breaking with worry and grief, our bodies aching with fatigue from lying awake by night and searching the city and trails for some sign of you by day?!" Joseph and the teachers remained stupefied. Jesus remained unmoved. I was having an effect on the adults present, but I was unable to touch my child.

Jesus eyed me calmly. "And why were you searching?" he said gently. "You know I have my Father's affairs to tend to." His words were not angry or reproachful, they simply pointed me back to the beginning of his life. This was not my son. I was God's slave, raising a child to whom I had no claim. His business was not as an artisan, a carpenter, or being my dutiful son. His business was of God. The anger drained from me. Tears continued to creep down over my cheeks. I was suddenly exhausted. The lack of sleep, the searching, the worry, and the shock of the Truth staring me in the face, consumed my last bit of energy. I remember thinking that maybe I could just slowly let myself down onto the floor of the temple. I no longer had the strength to continue standing. I looked at Jesus as if in a fog, as Joseph's strong arm slipped under mine and around my waist to support me. For the last ten years I had allowed myself to believe that this beloved child belonged only to Joseph and me. We had been devoted parents, but I had become possessive—and proud. I could feel the cold steel of Simeon's sword lying in my heart as darkness began to encircle my field of vision. I had faced the fact once again, that this child was destined for greater things than I could imagine, and I must not get in his way. I must support him, not cling to him. I must love him enough to let him be his Father's Son. Rising from the floor where he had sat at the feet of the teachers, Jesus came over, and putting his arm around me from the other side, began to help Joseph support me. The three of us moved slowly toward the gate that led out of the temple, while the still-stunned teachers watched in silence.

For three days, Jesus had been out of my sight, tending to the things of God. At the end of his life, he would again be out of my sight for three days, tending to the things of God. Then he would be taken from me to go to his Father's house, and I would see him no more in this life. Now Jesus' life prepared me for that end. It was a painful preparation, but it strengthened me for what was yet to come.

We sent word to Elizabeth and Zachariah that we had found Jesus safe and sound. We got food from one of the street vendors, and found a place to rest and eat. I began to feel stronger, so we started toward Jericho. We stopped part way, treating ourselves to a night in an inn. I had never slept so well. My son was safe—and he still loved me, even though I had gotten off track again. It was so easy to do.

We returned to Nazareth. Jesus was all that we could have wanted in a son and we watched in wonder as he grew wiser and stronger and reached manhood.

CHAPTER 9

The Wedding at Cana

Jesus remained at home for some time after he had officially reached manhood in the eyes of the rabbis, and I was grateful for his presence and strength. Joseph had died during Jesus' teen years,[1] and I was devastated. We had been through so much together. I will always marvel at the way in which he was able to simply accept God's will for his life. He is a model of faith for all people and was a model husband for me. His death left an emptiness in my life that I knew would never be filled. Without Jesus' presence, I do not know how I would have survived. He very capably became the head of the household; carrying on his father's trade, seeing to business, attending the synagogue—studying and learning[2]—it seemed that he was always learning! He thought deeply about life and righteousness,[3] his black eyes staring off into space. He would look at me and begin to discuss the things of God. I can still hear his deep, gentle voice speaking of the simplicity of our faith and how easy it is for people to be distracted from their relationship with God by all the different interpretations of scriptures and the different means of expressing piety. When they are distracted, the method of expressing their faith often becomes more important than the faith itself, which is all summed up, he said, in loving God and neighbor. If we would just stop hurting and judging one another and start helping and supporting and forgiving one another, leaning on our relationship with God for the strength to do his will, we

---

1. According to tradition, Joseph died when Jesus was still young. Joseph is never referred to after the incident at the Temple when Jesus was twelve.
2. In many of Jesus' teachings, he quotes or refers to the teachings of the rabbis and to oral tradition—an indication that Jesus was very well educated.
3. Biblically, righteousness is living in relationship with God, not keeping the law. Jesus fought the Pharisees' way of thinking, because their law-keeping got in the way of true righteousness. The law was given as a guide for living life with the least possible amount of pain. Jesus said, "The sabbath was made for man, not man for the sabbath." (Mark 2:27) The same could be said for the law, which we keep because of our respect for and love of God and because we trust that God knows what is best for us.

would find fulfillment in the simplicity of God's plan for us. "People need to be nice," he would chuckle, deep in his throat. Then his eyes would focus off in the distance as though he could see something that was out of range for me, and he would expand on what he had said using scripture and the teachings of the rabbis to illustrate his point. As I watched him and listened to his words, my heart would warm and swell with a feeling of importance as this wise son of mine—whom I had vaguely begun to feel that I no longer knew—would discuss religion with me, a woman.

Only Jesus would discuss religion with a woman. It was forbidden,[4] but that never seemed to bother him. Even as a child he would talk about God to the little girls that he played with. They would always stare at him quietly. I suppose they did not know quite how to react. We tried to teach him that our culture did not allow the discussion of religion with girls or women—they were to learn in their homes from their fathers or husbands[5]—but he would never take us seriously. "Girls are God's daughters and should be able to talk about God, too," he had said as a child. "It's a silly rule that keeps girls from talking and learning about God wherever they can." I had smiled then at the child-like simplicity and cuteness that I was confident he would outgrow. But now, as an adult, when Jesus talked with me, he would move from the subject of women to other nations and peoples, and I realized that his views on women were not something he would outgrow. They were beliefs that would continue to grow within him, expanding to include other nations. His were views that others would one day grow into. The Jews were God's chosen people, who were eventually to become ministers to the nations. All people would be God's people and as I listened to my son, I realized that, in Him, the time for that ministry had come.[6]

As Jesus neared thirty years of age,[7] he grew more and more restless. I knew that eventually life would change drastically for Jesus and for me. I watched him approach his thirtieth birthday with some anxiety, know-

---

4. Men did not discuss religion with women, except within the home where wives and daughters were taught what they needed to know. Jesus broke with tradition, discussing religion with Mary, the sister of Martha (Luke 10:38-42), the Samaritan woman at the well (John 4:7-30), and the woman who touched his robe to find healing (Matthew 9:20-22), etc.

5. Women were not credible witnesses—could not testify in a court of law—and could not teach about God or study about Him. They learned only as instructed by father or husband.

6. The woman at the well was a Samaritan. By including her, Jesus reached out to other nations. Later there was the Centurion, etc.

7. Men were not allowed to read or interpret scripture or to become a rabbi until the age of thirty.

ing that a change was coming; still, when it actually came, I was ill prepared.

Jesus had gone down to the southern part of the Jordan River near
Bethany where Zachariah's and Elizabeth's son John was preaching and
baptizing. Word had it that John was harshly criticizing the lives of God's
people—especially those in authority—calling them to repent of their sins
and be baptized as though they were pagans![8] There were also reports that
John had been dressing like a prophet of old, living in the desert, and eating strange foods that he found there, just as the great prophets had done
when they were preparing for something and needed to be strengthened
by God.[9] I had always known that John would be a rebel, but I never suspected that he would so completely disdain authority. He was verbally
attacking not only the religious power structure, but Rome as well. My
heart went out to his parents. They had waited for a child until their old
age, and now that child had grown into a man and he was not at all what
they had expected. Oh, they had expected him to be religious—had even
taken a Nazarite vow for him at birth, dedicating his life to God.[10] But
John had gone so far overboard!

It was not just that he had disappointed his parents; he was putting
himself in physical danger. The hard-line southern personality that was so
strong in him as a youth was sure to cause real trouble now. I was glad that
Jesus did not show signs of being a radical like John. My boy was a rebel in
his own right, but I was sure that he would follow more traditional lines
in teaching and living out his faith. (Little did I know!) Jesus and John had
enjoyed one another as boys even though they were very different, and I
thought that Jesus could help straighten out this poor old couple's son
now, before it was too late.

Jesus had been gone about two months. I was not worried, but I was
anxious to see him and to hear all about the time he had spent with John.
Some people who had been to Jerusalem had told me that Jesus was
spending time as one of John's disciples. I was so intent on Jesus changing

8. Baptism was used to bring non-Jews into the faith.
9. When the prophets went out into the desert, they were placing themselves in a situation where they had no choice but to depend entirely upon God for food and drink—for life
itself. And so a "desert experience," in which a person was stripped of all independence from
God, was a time when faith was strengthened, and the relationship with God became very intimate. (What circumstances in your life have been desert experiences?)
10. A Nazarite was dedicated to God. When John's parents made the vow it meant that
John would not drink alcohol, cut his hair, or have sexual intercouse with a woman. Samson also
was a Nazarite.

John's rebellious ways, that I thought it was just his clever way of going about doing it. I was truly shocked when Jesus came home a changed man.

I knew as soon as I saw him that things were different. He gave me his usual hug, only I sensed in him an air of authority as he moved and talked and laughed. But the thing that really struck me was the depth of quiet confidence that was his. It showed in the way he held himself, in the way he spoke, in the way he treated others—in everything about him. I could see that those searching, one-sided conversations he had carried on with me were over. He was no longer searching. He was now certain in his beliefs. He now spoke words with such a finality that there would be no disputing him. The reaction of the teachers in the temple had foreshadowed this development. Now it was here.

Jesus' new sense of presence had obviously given confidence to those around him, including me. I found the whole thing both comforting and frightening. I was comforted because it meant that my job was completed, and I had done what was required of me. Jesus had once believed strongly that the people had gotten off track in their thoughts and understanding of God. He had tried on several occasions to show others what he meant; now he *must* show the people the way. Nothing would stop him. I was frightened because I knew he would, without a doubt, lay down his life if necessary. The changes in him were that obvious!

You can imagine the rush of conflicting emotions I had. I knew that the time for Jesus to proceed with God's work had arrived, and I saw that he was ready. It was a time I had lived for and a time I had dreaded. I truly was God's slave, as I had told the angel, but I am also human. Can you imagine raising a child knowing that he will one day do great things for the world—greater things than anyone else has ever done, things that desperately need doing—but that by doing so, he will put himself in mortal danger? You can't help loving your child, even knowing that that love will someday bring pain, but when you know the pain is coming, that you are walking into it, you are almost tempted to not love. Parents who have sent sons and daughters off to war know that feeling as do the parents of children who lay their lives on the line for what is just and good. As you watch your child walk into harm's way, you consider that this may be the result of your teaching them to be good, caring people. If you have done your job well, then one day they may indeed lay down their lives, and you will have nothing left but memories. I had known deep in my soul since that fateful, joyous day in the temple with Simeon that my son would go through something that would hurt me terribly. I wanted to love him as a child—I couldn't help loving him—but I knew that love would one day bring great pain. My throat tightened and my eyes watered with pride and joy and grief when I saw his face that day—that day he came home from the south to take me to a friend's wedding. I never again hoped for or even thought about him reforming John!

Jesus showed up on a Tuesday with some disciples of his own. Some of them I had heard about because their families were prominent in the fishing industry on the Sea of Galilee. Most were strangers to me when they arrived that day, but they would not be strangers long. Jesus introduced them, and I had the feeling that we were all one big family. They came in and made themselves right at home, some of them sitting and some reclining on the floor. Jesus laid down flat on his back, folded his arms behind his head, and sighed. He looked up at me happily and smiled. He was as glad to be home as I was to have him there.

The men relaxed, talking and laughing. I listened as I began to prepare an evening meal for them. They began talking about their trip up to Nazareth. They spoke of things they had seen and done along the way. At first, Jesus joined in, but he gradually grew silent. The others didn't seem to notice. They were enjoying themselves. Then, after seeming to ponder deeply for a time, Jesus raised up on his elbow and spoke.

"You people haven't said anything about Scythopolis! How about that temple there?" There was a strange edge to his voice, and everyone looked at him. I stopped my work and stood looking in his direction. He laughed.

"Why are you all looking at me like that? I've always enjoyed that temple. It's not really a temple, I suppose… more of a stadium where the stories of Dionysus are retold through liturgy…a shrine, I guess you could say." Jesus paused. "I've always enjoyed the stories that were enacted in that stadium!" Jesus seemed perfectly relaxed now, ready to tell a story. The others still eyed him suspiciously, although they were beginning to relax. The edge to his voice was gone. I studied him carefully. I knew my boy. He was up to something. He was referring to one of the Greek gods. Our land was the sight of many of the stories about those gods, so we all knew their stories and lived in the midst of shrines built to honor them.

Grinning up at me, acknowledging that he knew that I knew that this was more than just a story, Jesus began to spin the tale of the god of the grapevine.

"Come on, everyone knows the stories of Dionysus—the only mortal born of a god!"

Jesus' words hit pretty close to home. The skin on my face tightened, tugging at my ears. Shocked, I gave my full attention to him. What was Jesus doing?! I looked at him. He smiled and went on.

"Dionysus has always been a favorite of the people. The story says that he was as yet unborn when his mortal mother died, and his father, Zeus, took him into his own body where he nourished him until his ninth month."

Leaning against the wall, I lowered myself to the floor. Supper could wait! I wanted to hear the rest of this.

"Dionysus' nurse was buried in our land, so this was a holy place for him, and he spent much time here. He planted grapevines in our hills and taught the people to tend them. As you know, the grapevine has literally been life to us![11] We could not survive in this rocky, hilly place without our vineyards. So we owe much to this legendary god!"

Jesus paused. Son of a god—one who brought life—what was he trying to say? I was puzzled by Jesus' persistence in telling this story. He was not oblivious to my puzzled look nor to the lack of interest shown by his disciples. He chuckled and went on.

"The god of the vine died a tragic death, being ripped apart piece by piece, but Zeus resurrected him and granted him eternal life. Once that was accomplished, Dionysus descended into hell in order to rescue his mother. From there he took her up into heaven to live forever. Although the people never see Dionysus anymore, they are reminded of him each spring when the grapevines, which appeared to be dead all winter, burst

---

11. God's people could not have lived in the desert hill country of Israel without the grapevine. The vine provided fruit for food, raisins, wine for drinking and medicine, vinegar for seasoning, antiseptic and medicine, and a syrup made from boiled-down grape juice—called honey in the Bible. Wood was scarce, so the vine was used for handles for doors, hoes, and sickles, braces for mud roofs, and other things where a small piece of wood would do. The tendrils and small branches were used for quick cooking fires and for weaving baskets. Leaves were used to wrap things in (like waxed paper for us) and to feed the donkey at the end of the dry season when other food sources were depleted. Having a vineyard was a lot of work. One had to build a stone wall to hold soil, bring the soil up from the valley, and, once the vines were planted, hoe the dew into the ground each morning of the dry season to keep the vines alive. But having a vineyard meant having life. When Jesus says he is the vine, he is speaking of the grapevine and of its and his necessity for life.

into new life. You see, Dionysus is resurrection and life to his followers! He is hope for all his people! He is comfort for those who have lost loved ones to death. And," Jesus' eyes twinkled with a secret knowledge, "we know that this story is true, because—although I have never seen it myself—the followers of Dionysus say that each year on January sixth, the water in the jars in the stadium—the temple of Dionysus—changes into wine!"

The men laughed at this last comment of Jesus and cheered his story. They began joking, bantering back and forth about the "god" Dionysus and all the other Greek "gods". I sat stunned. January sixth! That was the day the magicians had come to find my baby. My mind replayed the story Jesus had told. Dionysus. Son of a god. Giver of life. Died and resurrected. Descended to hell. Eternal life. Hope and comfort. What was Jesus saying? Why had he chosen this particular story to talk about? I struggled, but could make no sense of it. Perhaps he was just telling a story after all.

I rose to my feet and continued the preparation of the food, but my mind kept returning to the story. Then I saw Jesus glance at me with the look he had always given when he and I had shared a secret. He was quickly back to bantering with the men, leaving me with the knowledge that something was in the air, though I had no idea what.

Early the next morning we would leave for the wedding over in Cana. Many of our friends and relatives would be there, and I would get to spend the week with them and with Jesus. I went to sleep feeling warm and content that night. My child was home. It was a time to let go of worries and enjoy my happiness.

We left home at the first light of day on Wednesday morning. After making the short hike over to Cana, the men left me at the bride's home and went on to find the groom at his home. As I joined the other women, I thought, with some sadness, of the celebration Joseph and I had missed because of my pregnancy. Weddings were such big events with the feasting going on for a week. Everyone came, and everyone celebrated. My twinge of self-pity came and went very quickly. This bride was so excited. Her wedding had been arranged, but her parents had discussed it with her, as some did. She knew the groom. He was from a well-to-do family, and handsome, and kind, and gentle... she was quite pleased with him, already in love, which was nice but not necessary. Love came later for most couples, as they joined together in body and spirit facing life as one.

The bride had reached puberty, and it was time for her to marry and bring children into the world. She was fifteen, the same age I was when I moved in with Joseph. As I listened to the young bride chattering with her friends, the joy of those days flooded my soul once more. I felt again Joseph's strength and tenderness that had not only carried me through those difficult days, but had made life good for me as well. If only he could be here to see the fine son he had cared for!

Time went quickly and my reverie was soon broken by the sound of the men coming. The bride quickly covered her face with her veil. We women all gathered round her. We had bathed her and had washed her hair, braiding it and weaving family jewelry into it as we went. We had perfumed her and helped her put on the beautifully embroidered dress she had made for the occasion. Her betrothal coins were placed lovingly on her forehead where she would wear them throughout her married life. They were a symbol of her worth, as well as a "life insurance policy" in case something happened to her husband. We were all dressed in our wedding garments, and we waited anxiously. We heard the groom come to the door of the next room. He and the best man were welcomed into the home by the bride's father and his friend. Quickly, the final friendly haggling over the bride price began. The price had really already been set twelve months before at the betrothal, but the day would not be complete without this part of the ritual. The bride giggled. Her groom was paying a good price, which gave her a feeling of great worth. When the haggling was ended, the price was paid, as witnessed by the best man, and the father came into the room where the bride waited. He looked with pride at his precious daughter, and then, with tears in his eyes, he kissed her gently on the cheek. Then, taking her hand, he led her to the groom and stepped back. The groom looked at the bride only briefly before going back outside, where he mounted the white horse[12] that he would ride to his wedding. As his friends cheered him on, he began riding back toward his home. The bride had dutifully taken her position behind the horse and followed along to the joyous shouts of her friends. Jesus was among the men and our eyes met briefly as we joined in the shouting and cheering. Then the singing began and continued throughout the procession. It felt good to be enjoying life together.

12. Grooms rode a white horse or a white donkey.

The procession made its way through the narrow streets of Cana to the home of the groom. There the food had been prepared, the wine waited, and all was laid out for the party. The bride and groom retreated to the bridal chamber, the tent where the marriage would be consummated. The best man accompanied them. He would stand at the door and listen for the cry of the groom, serving as a witness that the marriage had taken place. When the couple emerged from their room with the sheets showing the signs of the bride's virginity, the celebration began in earnest. Wine was poured, and the toastmaster of the celebration offered a toast to the young couple. With cheering, the wine was consumed, and the food was brought by the servants. The people feasted and talked and laughed. Joy ran high!

But then, as the party was progressing nicely, I began to sense that something was wrong. The servants were buzzing and flitting around, and I saw them going to the parents of the wedding couple. It became evident that they were talking about the wine. Evidently the supply was running low, and the parents were very concerned. The bride and groom caught wind of what was happening, and I could see the looks of disbelief. It was a disgrace to run out of wine in the middle of a wedding celebration, especially here in the hills of the Galilee where some of the finest dry white wine in the world was produced—wine that was shipped to far reaches of the empire because of its quality. Here in the midst of such renown, to run out of wine?! The family members were beside themselves. Evidently, there was some mistake about the amount that was ordered, and now it was nearly gone!

Surely Jesus could help, I thought. He and his friends could go quickly and buy more. It would still leave some awkward moments, but it made sense to send these strong young men to take care of things. I walked over to Jesus, wasting no time. "Son," I said, "they have no wine!"

Then with a mixture of humor, teaching, and rebuke, he answered. "Woman," he said.

WOMAN!? I was shocked and insulted! Jewish boys did not call their mothers, woman! It was not *just* an insult. It was... well, unheard of!

Jesus went on. "Woman, what is it to you?! And to me?!"

I was speechless! Was he now telling me to shut up and be quiet?!

"My hour has not yet come!" he continued.

I was stunned. I knew there was more than insult intended. He was joking with me and teaching me ... but what? I was glad that no one else had heard, and, in an attempt to act like nothing was happening, I turned to the servants and said, "Do whatever he tells you!" as if it were all a joke. In reality, though, my head was reeling, and, having given orders to the servants, I turned to my own thoughts.

"Woman!" He had called me woman! Jesus was not a rude or disrespectful son. What was he saying to me? And why now, when we were having such a good time together? "Woman!" I was sure that my face was red with anger, but I continued to think, struggling to find Jesus' meaning. Something was going to happen, or he would not have challenged me like this. "Woman!" It made me think of Eve, the mother of all life. She was woman. And through her, sin came into the world. Her sin was control. She wanted to be in charge, deciding for herself what God wanted from her. Then I realized that, like Eve, I was trying to be in control again.

Through "woman," through Eve, came all life. With repentant hope, I thought that perhaps all life now came through me—at least all life that mattered. Jesus was on the verge of bringing new things—new thoughts—new life, into the world. And he had come from my body. Perhaps he was reminding me that, although I had played a very important role, I must now stand aside and not try to control God. It was so hard to let go when it was my little boy—become a man—that God was using to bring new life to the world.

I knew that what God was trying to accomplish through my son would not be done easily. Old Simeon's sword took a little twist, and my moist eyes met Jesus'. He smiled a tender smile of encouragement, then winked, as if to say, "Watch this."

Nearby stood several large stone jars that were used in purification ceremonies. While I had been struggling with my own thoughts, Jesus had ordered the jars filled with water. That was about 150-200 gallons, but the jars were filled very quickly with rainwater that was stored on the roof nearby. Only "water from heaven" could be used for purification ceremonies, and now that same water was poured into the waiting jars until they were filled to the brim. Jesus watched me, as the servants drew water from the jars and took it to the toastmaster of the feast. I glanced at him, and his eyes danced with joy and mischief.

Then I heard the toastmaster saying, "Most people serve the best wine first, and when the people are drunk, bring out the poor wine. But you have saved the best for now!" The crowd roared at the joke, and the parents and the wedding couple laughed laughs of confusion. They were out of wine! Was the toastmaster making fun of them?! But then the servants poured some of the water into the cups of the wedding party, and their laughs changed to laughs of relief and joy. Their party was saved! They didn't know how, but it was saved!

I was the one who was confused now, still not realizing that the water had become wine. Servants were filling cups all around from the water jars, and smiles and nods and exclamations of joy followed as people tasted from their freshly filled cups. I looked back at the wedding party. The parents and the couple looked slightly confused, but very happy! The bride and groom looked into one another's eyes and gave each other a quick hug! Their eyes were wet. There was no longer any trace of embarrassment on their faces.

Then someone handed me a cup of the water, except that it was not water at all! It was wine! The party was escalating around me. The water had been changed into wine! The noise of the party grew louder as I stood stunned!

I began to try to put things together. Woman?! Water from wine? I was gripped with disbelief and confusion. In the midst of the wild celebration, I looked toward Jesus. Our eyes met once again. The mischief drained from him and a tender seriousness flooded his face. The corners of his pursed lips turned up briefly in a half smile. He loved me—of that he left no doubt, and he knew I was having trouble dealing with who he was and what all this meant.

Order was emerging from all God's actions throughout Jesus' life, but I was not sure I liked the new order. My baby had just turned water into wine! "Oh, dear God!" My mind raced. "Dionysus! Water to wine!" Jesus was using the story to teach us about himself. Dionysus was a legend, created in the minds of humans, showing those things they would like a god to be. Jesus was created by God, to show people what God is. And the similarities were astounding. I remembered the thoughts I had had about Dionysus as Jesus had told the story. "Son of a god"—yes, Jesus was that. "Giver of life"—I was sure he would be, but I did not yet know how. "Died a horrible death and resurrected!" At that thought, Simeon's sword pierced my soul again. Was that what Simeon had seen? A horrible death awaiting my son? My mind did not move on to thinking of resurrection and life. It had stopped at "horrible death!"

My eyes searched the crowd looking for Jesus, who was mingling with the guests. I saw his disciples. They were standing near the edge of the crowd, and they had obviously been thinking, too. Now they looked toward Jesus. There was a new sense of respect written on their faces. Now they obviously saw Jesus in a new way, not just as a peer with whom to joke and from whom to learn. Jesus had used the story of Dionysus to teach them who he really was. Son of God. Giver of life. Source of hope … Now they believed in something they had hardly dared hope for—the Son of God and he had changed water into wine![13]

My eyes found Jesus. He was standing on the edge of a group of people laughing and enjoying the festivities. Even so, he carried that new air of seriousness and confidence that I had sensed in him when I first saw him after his return from the South. I knew the time had come. Jesus was ready to show his hand! My mind was racing. But his hour had not yet come! Simeon's sword twisted in my heart! "Dear God, help me," I prayed. My son was setting his face in a direction that would pierce my heart in ways that I could not even imagine! It was too much! Everything seemed to be growing dark, but it was early. My ears began to buzz, and the world took on a quality of unreality. What was happening?

Jesus looked in my direction and then moved quickly toward me. The celebration around me was moving into the distance of my mind. The sounds seemed so far away …then I could see only Jesus' eyes, and they began to fade… I felt his strong hand grip my arm.

"Mother…MOTHER!" he hissed. "Please! The wedding party! Mother…we'll talk! But not now…please!"

I wanted to relax and let his hand support me and not face the reality of what was happening. But he shook me hard and quick. I was jolted back to the present, and the party began growing louder again. I remember thinking it was funny how things faded in and out. Jesus' eyes looked down into mine. The love and concern I saw in them, coupled with his grave determination to bring me back to the festivities, overwhelmed me. I clamored out of the spiraling unreality that had gripped me briefly.

"Oh, my son!" I gasped, fully present once again.

"It was for this that I came, Mother!"

---

13. Seeing Jesus' first miracle, the disciples believed or trusted (the Greek can be translated either way) in him. (John 2:11)

"I know. I know." Tears began to well up.

"The guests, Mother! The party! We must share their joy now! Later we can talk!"

"Yes," I answered. "Yes," pumping life back into my soul. The bride and groom. Nothing must mar their joy. My son had chosen their wedding for his first miracle. I would rejoin their celebration! Yes, I would.

Jesus' disciples were excited by what had happened, but they were not moved in the same way that I had been. They had seen a supernatural act and, although they related it to Dionysus, they did not think much about the implications involved. Instead, they saw what they wanted to see. And, although Jesus told them later what I already knew—that living out the course he had set that day would one day cost him his life—they refused to hear. He could change water into wine! He could not die! He would be king, and they would be his right-hand men!

Yes, he would be king indeed! But the reality for me that day was that he would be a king who must die, and I would be his lonely grieving mother!

By the time the wedding was finally over and the people were beginning to head back to their homes, everyone was aware of what had happened. Water had been turned into wine. And whether or not individuals actually believed that water had turned to wine, they made the connection to Dionysus. As a good rabbi, Jesus had used the stories of Dionysus to teach who he was. In retrospect, people realized that Jesus was not just saving a young couple from embarrassment on their wedding day, but he was saying to all who would pay attention, "I am the real thing. My water really does change to wine—fine wine. I am born of a God, the only true God. I am the resurrection and life. I am the one who will conquer death for each of you." When the connection was made in the minds of people, they flocked to hear Jesus whenever he was in their area. Once things got started—and the wedding was the beginning—his ministry grew like wildfire.

"My hour has not yet come." He was speaking of the day when this would all come to light and be accomplished—completed. Again on that day he would call me "Woman!" to tell me it was finished—that what God had chosen me to do was done—that what the first Eve had effectively derailed, my willingness to be God's slave had been used to put back on track. He would call me woman to remind me of this joyous wedding day, the only other time he had dared to call me woman. Then I would remember what had happened here today and be reassured and have hope as I sat at the foot of the cross, witnessing the blood that was shed to effect the marriage between God and God's people for all time. That wedding blood would be seen on communion linens again and again down through the ages as people came to the altar to be united in an intimate relationship with God.

Jesus provided instruction for me in strange and subtle ways, but always, he provided.

CHAPTER 10

Saying Goodbye

After the wedding, Jesus and his disciples and I went over to Capernaum to relax for a few days. I was so glad to have some extra time with my son, and it was exciting to think of being in Capernaum! The city, located on the northwestern shore of the Sea of Galilee near a trade route, was both a pleasant and interesting place to visit. The small sea[1] kept temperatures comfortable. A cooling breeze came off the water by day, bringing relief from the heat. At night the breeze switched directions and blew onto the lake, coaxing from the soil and rocks the heat that the sun had hidden there by day, thus warming the chilly nights. The caravans that came to barter for supplies and to rest for the night provided all the wonders that people from far-off lands can bring. The dress and customs of different people varied, and the goods they carried...well, some we had seen but never owned; some we had only heard of; and some were simply beyond our imagining.

Peter and Andrew, who were at the wedding with us, had grown up in Capernaum and had homes and a family business there. Their business was quite unique, for their family was one of only a few that owned fishing rights on the Sea of Galilee. The fish caught there were highly prized; freshwater fish were a rarity in that part of the world. Those fish that were not sold locally were pickled and shipped to the far reaches of the empire. The brothers, Peter and Andrew, were wealthy businessmen who worked very hard.

It was in the home of Peter that we found a gracious welcome for those few days following the wedding. There we were able to relax and enjoy one another's company. For Jesus and me it was a very special time, for it was, in a way, a farewell. He was at the beginning of his ministry,

---

1. Actually a lake by size, the Sea of Galilee is thirteen miles long and eight miles wide at its longest and widest points. It is a fresh water lake.

and he would be leaving me behind. He wanted to talk before he left.[2]

It was after the midday meal on our second day in Capernaum that Jesus motioned for me to come with him. The others were going to rest during the heat of the day, and we could talk undisturbed. Going outdoors to a stone bench against the side of the house we sat next to one another feeling the refreshing breeze coming off the water and enjoying the shade of an ancient tree that grew there. We were silent for a bit, just enjoying the breeze, the shade, and one another's presence. As we sat quietly, my mind drifted back to other times. Since the days when he was a small child, Jesus had always taken me outside to the stone bench beside the house when he had something serious to discuss, and conversations of those past years filtered through my mind.[3]

Many were the times that Jesus had wanted to talk about the little boy next door who always seemed to want to pick a fight. He would push Jesus or call him names or punch him for no apparent reason, and Jesus struggled with how to respond. One particular time stood out in my mind. Jesus was about eight, and he had come home frustrated nearly to tears. "I just want to do something back to him. Maybe if I just hit him once—right in the nose!" he had said, his little determined face looking up at me.

"Then how would you teach him to love?" I had replied. "Remember King David and how Saul kept trying to kill him? David must have wanted to kill Saul, too, but instead he returned good for evil,[4] because that's what God wanted him to do."

Jesus would think about whatever I said. Then we would pray for God to strengthen him to do the right thing, and he would go running off to play again.

My mind continued drifting. There had been a conversation when Jesus was about nine concerning a little squirrel whose mother had been killed by some wild dogs. Jesus had brought the baby home and hoped he could convince us to let him keep it. Joseph and I had already talked of finding a pet of some kind for Jesus, but we had not told him. He was so serious and worked so hard at convincing me that he should be allowed to

2. Jesus and his mother and disciples did go to Capernaum after the wedding at Cana (John 2:12). The rest is imaginary, an attempt to understand what life was like for Mary and Jesus, considering the type of relationship they must have had as mother and son.

3. Mary must have had memories as all mothers do. These are a few speculations.

4. The story of Saul and David was (and still is among the Jews) used to teach of God's desire that we return good for evil.

keep the baby squirrel that I never told him about our plans. I just let him be pleased with himself, thinking he had convinced us.

Frequently, Jesus wanted to talk about his studies. He would come home excited about something he had learned at synagogue school, and I would listen. How I enjoyed those conversations! I smiled.

"Remembering my childhood, Mother?" Jesus asked, smiling down at me. His deep, soft voice brought me back to the present. I smiled up at him. He gave me a hug, and his smile disappeared. What we were about to discuss was far more serious than childhood quarrels or baby squirrels or school. As he began, he talked with the same confidence he had always had when he came to talk to me, knowing that even if I did not agree with him, I would listen and try to understand.

"I was baptized by John while I was down in the South, Mother." He paused, looking down at me, an almost teasing look in his eyes for a brief moment. He knew how I felt about the way John was living. "The Holy Spirit came upon me in my baptism," he continued. "You know that throughout the history of our people, whenever God's spirit came upon a person, that person's life changed drastically." He grinned accusingly, "Yours certainly did!" Then he grew serious again. "Now *my* life must change drastically, too." I knew it was true. I had always known. "In some ways," he went on, "my life will be the same. I will continue to live as God's child, and pray that my life will be pleasing to God." Looking down at me, no trace of teasing or smile left in his eyes, he cautioned, "There will be those who will not believe that. They will see me as opposing God instead of serving Him."

I was not at all sure that I wanted to hear what he had to say now. I struggled with wanting to shut him out—not wanting to know that he would now be in harm's way—not wanting Simeon's sword for myself, but I continued to listen. As I listened I began to feel distant, as though I were listening to him from some far away place. I had known this time would come, but had always denied it, because I did not want to give him up. Now the time had come, and I could not escape its consequences. Granted, he was thirty years old, and that alone meant changes for him. It meant that he had fulfilled his obligation to me as the eldest son. And it meant that he was now of an age when he would be allowed to read and study the scriptures[5] on his own. No longer would he just listen to others teach. Now he would become a teacher of God's Word. And he would teach not just by what he said, he would teach the Word to others by his very life.

I did not doubt that Jesus would still care about me, but now he was bound to other commitments, another life, a life separate from the one he had lived with me.

"I'd like you to stay here in Capernaum, Mother,"[6] he said. "I've found a place where you could live near the families of my friends. I need to know that the people I trust are looking out for you, so I won't worry." He was silent a moment, his face serious, almost grave. "I think you'd be safer here. I'd rather you did not go back to Nazareth. That part of our life is over."

His eyes studied me as I nodded. He was concerned about my safety! This I had not expected! It had never occurred to me that *I* must leave Nazareth, that *I* might be in danger.

"Mine will not be an easy life, Mother, and you won't be there for me to talk to. I'm going to miss you!" he said, his throat sounding a little thick. "We won't be spending time together like we always have in the past." He looked at me with sad, hopeful eyes—eyes that longed for a mother to accept what he was saying. He wanted my blessing, my approval, even though he must go ahead with God's plan with or without my support.

We sat in silence for a while. How could I reassure this son of mine that, even though it hurt to see him go, I understood. And, indeed, he had my blessing. Perhaps it would help if he knew that I was not surprised by what he was saying.

"I've always known this time would come, Jesus," I said, looking up at him. I saw relief in his eyes. "And I know it will not be easy for either you or me. I've known from the time you were a baby." The feeling of being distanced began to disappear as I went on, telling Jesus of past events, reminding myself as well.

"When you were forty days old, we went to the temple for my

5. Men could not read and study the scriptures on their own, or teach them, until they reached the age of thirty. Then, those who had shown promise were allowed to read a portion in Synagogue and expound on it—as Jesus did in Nazareth (Mark 6:1-6, Matthew 13:54-58).

6. Early in his ministry, Jesus relocated to Capernaum, which now calls itself, "the home town of Jesus." Apparently, his mother moved there, too. We recall that early in his ministry, the people of Nazareth rejected Jesus (Matthew 13:54-58, Mark 6:1-6).

purification and to dedicate you. I've told you before about old Simeon and how he frightened me nearly to death by snatching you out of my arms." We both laughed a little, remembering the story and how, as a small boy, Jesus had begged to hear it again and again. Sobering, I turned to face Jesus and went on.

"There was a part of the story I never told you, Jesus. In fact, I never told anyone, not even your father, even though he sensed that I had heard something that day that …" I searched for the right words. "…I knew was true, but wanted to deny." Jesus looked surprised. He remembered the special relationship that Joseph and I had had. Ours had been a good marriage.

"I never felt that I should share this part with him," I said, "and when he died while you were still young, I understood why he was not to know. There was no need. He would have known pain in anticipation of something he would not live to see.

"The truth is, after Simeon had sung his song, he leaned close to me, and as he was putting you back into my arms, he told me that you were destined to cause many to fall and rise in Israel! You were to be a sign that would be opposed, so that the inner thoughts of many would be revealed.[7] I have never completely understood that part, although I think it will become clear as you begin your ministry. The last part I understood. He said, 'and a sword will pierce your own soul, too,' and it did, right then and there, as I realized that my precious little baby boy would someday hurt in ways that I would learn about only in time. A mother cannot see her child hurt, or even think of his being hurt, without experiencing pain herself." I sought his eyes once again. "I know that you are right in what you are about to do."

Jesus looked at me with wonder.

"You never told me these things before," he said.

"I didn't want to frighten you," I said, with sorrow. "I wanted your childhood to be a happy one." I managed a half-smile.

I could see Jesus' eyes searching the past. Shortly, he spoke. "That explains the sadness I saw in your eyes at times when I was very young, and you would hug me, and we would feel so close," he said. "I could never understand why you looked so sad, when we felt so full of love for

---

7. Luke 2:34-35 As people recognize their sinfulness, they fall (into despair, guilt, etc.), but as they recognize the forgiveness of a loving God, they rise again. Some react to having their sin revealed with humility and repentance, others with denial and anger, some of those, striking out.

one another."

"It was hard holding your little body close and remembering that the time would come when I would have to give you up. I was to love you and care for you, so that you could leave me and willingly enter a life that would be filled with danger. I never understood why it would be dangerous, but I knew it would."

"Oh, Mother! Thank you for everything." Jesus hugged me and sighed. "You've always been the one person that understood!" He sat with one arm around my shoulder. "I know it hasn't been easy, and..." he paused, and as he pulled his arm back to his own side and clasped his hands in his lap, I could see tears creeping into his clear, black eyes, "...it's only going to get harder." He looked down at me. "Sometimes I long to just stay home and be your son," he said. Tears came to my eyes then. How I longed for it, too, but I knew it could not be. He paused for a moment. "The way is going to get really rough now." I nodded. We sat quietly for a while, each feeling the warmth of the other's presence and wishing it didn't have to end. "Some of what I am going to have to do, you will not understand," he said sadly. "Please remember the things we've talked about today when you doubt me, and then try to trust."[8] Again he looked at me with those sad, hopeful eyes that had always been able to touch my heart.

"I'll do my best," I promised. "But how could I ever not trust you?" As soon as I said it, I remembered all the times my mind had wavered back and forth—especially the time Jesus had stayed behind at the temple when he was a boy, and now the time at the wedding we had just come from. We looked at each other and a smile crept into Jesus' eyes. Then we both burst into laughter. We knew I had doubted him before, and I would doubt him again. It felt good to laugh together and break the tension of such a serious moment.

We sat in silence for a little while, and then Jesus returned to talking. He told me many things. He spoke of his baptism again, and how, after he was baptized, God's spirit had come upon him as a dove lighting upon the ground. I pictured one of those beautiful creatures coming through the air and then fluttering and flapping, hovering over the ground, stirring all that is beneath it, before it lands. I reflected that once long ago, on that first of all days, the same spirit had, like this small beau-

---

8. Jesus said, "Believe in God, believe also in me," which is the same as saying, "Trust in God, trust also in me." Wherever and whenever Mary heard Jesus say, "Trust me!" she must have heard it, and she needed to remember it later on.

tiful flying symbol of life and peace,[9] fluttered and flapped and hovered over the earth in creation, stirring the waters beneath it and creating new things. Later, it had stirred and created new things in me, and now—in Jesus.

Jesus went on to tell me how he had been tempted to run as he began to understand what lay ahead for him in his new life. "My first inclination," he said, "was to simply return to Nazareth and continue in Father's business, supporting and caring for you. I thought I could build up my carpentry trade, eventually open some extra shops around the country—here in Capernaum and in Sephoris—places where the wealth is. Perhaps, I could even become wealthy, control my own little portion of the world and give you all that you deserve."[10] He glanced at me lovingly. "When I thought about doing that, though, I felt a strong reassurance that you would be cared for in some other way." I reached over and took his hand. I smiled my reassurance for I, too, knew that I would somehow be provided for.

Jesus went on talking. "Then I was tempted to go to the other extreme. Instead of running, I thought of just grabbing the power that seems to be mine and using it to win the people's favor or to take control of the government—to establish God's kingdom by might, by miracles, by whatever it took—once and for all time and have it done. I knew that was not the way God wanted it done, but surely God would not desert me. I could just go ahead, planning the way myself, and trusting God to back me up." I frowned. Trying to manipulate God is no small sin. Jesus noted my frown and smiled briefly. "I know that no kingdom established through force and control has ever lasted very long. And I know that I must do things according to God's schemes, not my own.

"Then the Spirit led me into the Judean wilderness. That place is so hot and dry and desolate, I don't know how John can bear to live there!"

9. Doves were very symbolic to the ancient people. In the desert land of Jesus, if people were seeking life-giving water, they would watch for doves, which would lead them to water, so doves naturally became a symbol of life. The dove was believed to lack a gall sack, and therefore was a symbol of purity. It was also a symbol of peace, since these birds are non-aggressive and can be approached with little difficulty. Thus, the dove seems a perfect symbol of the Holy Spirit.

10. Jesus' temptations in the wilderness were the universal temptations of humankind: control people, control God, and control one's own destiny (i.e., self as center—forgetting God's warning, "Beware, lest you say in your heart, 'my power and the might of my hand have gotten me this wealth.'" (Deuteronomy 8:17) He would have experienced these temptations at other times, as well. Here (I speculate) he is tempted to make control of his own destiny and control of people his goal instead of having service of God as his goal. He goes on to consider controlling God, as well.

Jesus reflected silently for a moment, then went on. "I stayed there a long time,[11] Mother, without food or water." The thought gave me shivers. Life is so fragile in that desert. I am glad that I did not know, at the time, that he was there. A simple shift in the wind could have brought his death!

Jesus continued, "I was tempted beyond anything I ever thought I could resist, but each time that I was tempted, I was given just enough strength to resist. Just enough. No more and no less!

"When the temptations had passed, I left the wilderness." Shifting his weight and leaning forward, as he had always done as a child when he was about to tell me something he had learned that amazed him, he went on. "Now I understand why people have always gone to the desert when they needed to draw near to God. While I was out there, I learned to depend completely on God for everything, including survival itself. I think that I will be able to stay dependent on God and do everything the way he wants it done; because I know that God will give me whatever I need to sustain me, when I am living according to his will. I know now that God is not leading me in the ways of military might or victory through working miracles. Instead, He wants me to establish his kingdom through gentleness and love, for then it will be a kingdom that will last forever, not just for a few generations."

Jesus' words had implications that I had never considered. I sat there astonished and silent. Jesus squeezed my hand, and looking up, I saw that he had tears in his eyes, as did I. But as we sat there together, we both knew that our tears on this day were much more than tears of sadness. They were tears of being moved by the knowledge that together as mother and son, we were caught in the middle of a movement, a preordained plan, that was so profound and universal in nature, that I could not begin to comprehend it. They were tears of knowing that the time had come for me to let go of Jesus, and for him to let go of me, in the sense that he could no longer be my son in human terms. And they were tears of knowing a peace that lay beneath all our fears and wrapped them in a warm blanket of unshakable hope, making them insignificant.

We took one last long look and gave one another a sad, yet joyous, hug. It was for this that I had lived, and it was for this that Jesus had come

---

11. Jesus was in the wilderness forty days. Forty, in the Bible, means a lot or a long time—not literally forty. Forty days was a long time—a lot of days (rain in Noah's time, Moses on the mountain with God). Forty years (Moses and the people in the wilderness) was a long time—a lot of years.

into the world. We both knew that Jesus had set in motion a direction, a course of action from which there was no turning back, even if he ended up like the other 'messiahs!' The life he would live from now on would benefit all nations—but at great cost to both of us. The tears in our eyes were tears of goodbye, yet they were also tears of hello.

CHAPTER 11

Who is My Mother?

Shortly after our talk, Jesus headed for Jerusalem. It was the time of Passover, and he would now begin his ministry in earnest. He reassured me that he would be back and would expect his favorite home-cooked meal when he came. We laughed at that, embracing one another, and then, through my tears, I proudly watched him walk away. How I loved this man who had been the center of my life for the past thirty years.

As the weeks and months passed, Jesus' work took him back and forth between Jerusalem and Galilee.[1] Sometimes, when he was in the area, I would see him, and, sometimes, I would not. But, always, I would hear rumors about what he was doing. I was never sure what was actually true, and what had been exaggerated and twisted. So, when I did see Jesus, I would ask him about the things that troubled me, but his answers were not always comforting. For example, he told me that what I had heard about his deliberately breaking the Sabbath on several occasions[2] was true. That shocked me. Jesus had always been so serious about keeping God's law and had always observed the Sabbath. But he quickly pointed out to me that it was not God's law that he was breaking, but rather an interpretation of it.[3] He had been doing good on the Sabbath, healing people, in order to call attention to the spirit of the law.

"After all," he had said, "the Sabbath was made for people, not people for the Sabbath. Should it not be permissible to do good on the Sabbath?" Then he went on to talk about how the ultra-religious among God's people were using religion for power, control, prestige—a means of keeping themselves separate from those with whom they wanted no con-

1. Galilee was the northern region that included the Sea of Galilee and Nazareth.
2. John 5:9, Matthew 12:1, Mark 3:2, Luke 13:10, etc.
3. Many laws had been set up surrounding the Law given by God in an attempt to "put a fence" around the Law and keep people from breaking it. They might break the interpretive laws, but those would keep them from breaking God's law. The Mishnah contains these extra laws.

tact anyway. These radicals had become very legalistic and had lost their sense of compassion. So, instead of teaching God's laws as a way of getting along—a way of helping one another to have a good life, a way of showing our love for God, the law had become a burden that was impossible for a caring person to keep in its entirety. And since it was those who appeared so "holy"—who wore their religion for all to see—that said the law must be kept to the finest letter, some of the common people felt a lot of pressure to do exactly that.

"Remember when the little neighbor boy fell into that old well on the Sabbath? That was a badly broken arm he had, and he was in mud and water in the darkness at the bottom of that pit. Have you forgotten the hollow sound of his frightened cry coming out of the well?" Jesus looked me in the eye.

I remembered the situation well. Some of the people of Nazareth had pressured the parents to keep the interpretation of the law as set forth by the Mishnah.[4] According to it, the boy's parents should leave him there until the Sabbath was over. They could do as much as possible to make him comfortable, but since his actual life was not endangered by staying in the well, they were to leave him there. Like most of our wells, this one was just a deep cistern that collected rainwater—and spiders! Most people never noticed the spiders, but they were there, lurking in the deep crevices! Of course, the little boy was frightened, and he was in pain! And he wanted his parents! And he cried out! But moving him would be work, and working would be breaking the Sabbath. Jesus watched me as I thought.

"They took him out," I said.

"And there were those who never let them forget that they 'broke the law.' I never could blame the parents for saying they wanted nothing to do with a god who wanted them to let their son suffer, when it was in their power to help him.

"Anyway, if it had been their ox or donkey that had fallen into the well, they could have done whatever was necessary to get it out, because that had to do with their livelihood. But their own little boy, they were

---

4. A collection of religious and cultural practices written down over a period of about four centuries, beginning around 2 B.C., by the Scribes and the teachers of the Oral Law. The latter was in keeping with the teachings of the Pharisees.

expected to allow to suffer![5]

"Couldn't those self-satisfied, judgemental people see that love is action, not feeling!? That if they loved that little boy as God had commanded them to do, they would have no choice but to act on his behalf, to lift him out of that frightening pit and relieve his pain!"

Pausing, Jesus sighed. He obviously felt better for having voiced what was bothering him. Now he went on at a calmer and slower pace, explaining what he was trying to do. He reminded me that God's teaching was intended to show us how to go about loving God and one another. He believed we had gotten away from that idea—not that it was the first time in the history of God's people. It had happened over and over again as recorded in the Prophets. He said, "Granted, we don't need God to tell us to love those who love us or those with whom we agree, but we do need God's law to help us love those who don't love us and those with whom we disagree. And if our disagreement concerns religion, all the more reason that our love should bridge the gap between us. We are all God's people." His voice trailed off, and he was silent for so long that I thought he was finished, but then he looked up at me unhappily. "People are using God's teachings for judging and hurting one another instead of for loving. We are supposed to be setting one another free to live life at its fullest and best, instead of turning the law into a cumbersome burden that makes life difficult and painful." He stopped and sat quietly. Then, "We are saved—made whole and complete[6]—when we are being ourselves to our fullest and best. We were each one created in God's image, so when we are ourselves, we are what we were created to be. We need to be set free from all the rules that keep us from loving, from all the teachings that keep us from the oneness with God that both frees us to be ourselves and comes of being ourselves. Rules that judge and hurt, and people that judge and hurt, are keeping people from God."

"I know you're right," I said. "A lot of us have known these things for a long time. And I know that you need to do something about it." I swallowed hard to keep the tears back. "It's just that I wish you could

5. A fictitious incident illustrating the explanation of the Biblical law as it is recorded in the Mishnah. One was allowed to help an injured person on the Sabbath only enough to save the life. Any other help must wait until the Sabbath ended.

6. Salvation has a great deal more to do with becoming whole people than with heaven or hell. One of the root words means to enlarge—hence, to deliver. We may be delivered from bondage, sin, death, etc., and in the process become more nearly ourselves, i.e. who we were created to be.

make changes by working more within the accepted structures."

Jesus took my hand and squeezed it. He sighed. "I wish it could be that way, too," he whispered.

As time went by, I heard more and more reports about what Jesus was doing. I was sure he was being misrepresented by a twisting of the truth, and that concerned me, but what concerned me most was the building pressure under which he had to be working. We like to think that if a person will just do things God's way, then everyone will love that person and support them, but it is not so. It never has been. Like the prophets of old, Jesus was not accepted by a number of people, and he had to be very careful about whom he trusted. Some people opposed him with a passion because his teaching threatened the organized religion to which they had devoted their lives and through which many of them earned a living. These people were the most dangerous of those who opposed him, because of the influence they exerted both with our people and with Rome.[7] They had the power to bring charges against him for such things as blasphemy, which was punishable by death. Among this opposition were those who feared that Jesus' popularity would attract the attention of Rome, and that Rome would see him as a revolutionary with a growing following and bring in military force to destroy him and his followers and anyone else who happened to get in the way.

Less dangerous were the people who shied away from Jesus just because he was doing something different. They listened briefly to his teaching, and then shut it out because it would mean change, and change can be frightening and difficult. Others, who had known Jesus for years, could not accept the fact that he was a prophet—simply because they knew him. They rejected him without even giving him a chance.

Still others rejected him because of the people he did not turn away, but rather welcomed. Jesus spoke of these on one occasion when he admitted to me that he did have friends among sinners (as we called tax collectors and prostitutes). There were tax collectors among his followers—those traitors who had gone over to Rome in order to get rich at the expense of their own people. Yes, some, who were prostitutes when Jesus

---

7. After the Babylonian exile, the priests had become the ruling class, responsible for the people, and answerable to the ruling nation—in Jesus' time, Rome. The first of these priests was Simon of the Maccabees. Neither he nor those who followed him were trained to be priests, neither were they particularly pious.

met them, were counted among his disciples. Besides that, Jesus admitted, he had traveled through Samaria, stopping at Jacob's well to discuss theology with a Samaritan—a woman, no less! He even drank after her. I was shocked by *all* this—but Samaritans? We never set foot in Samaria because we did not associate with Samaritans.[8] They practiced an offshoot of our religion that we did not accept. We did not eat or drink from their vessels, since that would make us unclean. And, of course, men did not talk to women, especially about religion.

I saw Jesus less frequently as time went by. When I did see him, he would sometimes talk of the things I had heard that troubled me. He would remind me that all people are God's people—created in His image and consequently of great worth. When people are loved—accepted unconditionally—they are able to recognize their own worth and are then able to grow and become all that God has created them to be. I actually met some of the tax collectors and prostitutes, and I could see that it was true. They were people who had changed, people who now reached out to others with that love and concern that had been extended to them. It was amazing the difference that came about in people simply because of the healing love they knew in Jesus' presence. When I was in his presence, I knew that healing love, too, and I knew that whatever he did, it would be the right thing.

It was when he was gone, and I was not in his presence, that I would begin to wonder. I would hear about the healings, the feeding of multitudes, the walking on water and stilling of storms, the crowds following after him. I even heard that, just as Jesus had used Dionysus to teach about himself at the wedding in Cana, he had also used the story of Esclepius in Jerusalem. What he was saying there, if the reports were right, would further turn people against him—as if he needed more enemies!

It seemed he had gone to the shrine erected to Esclepius at the sheep gate in Jerusalem. The water in the pool there would occasionally bubble and boil, and the pool would be stirred up. There were always a lot of sick people around the pool, because they believed that the first person who got into the water when it was troubled would be healed. When Jesus

8. Samaritans were the result of intermarriage that occurred after the northern kingdom, Israel, was conquered by Assyria. Many of the people were carried off into exile, and people from other lands were brought in to replace them. Marriages between those left in Israel and the foreigners who were brought in resulted in the Samaritans. They still worshipped the one true God, but were rejected because of the intermarriage and because they recognized Mt. Gerizim as the place of worship and where the Messiah would appear rather than the temple mount.

arrived at the pool, he found a man who had been waiting for thirty-eight years for someone to put him into the pool at the right time. This man, who had been there for so long, never had anyone to put him in, so he just lay there hoping that someday he would somehow get into the water and be healed. Jesus healed him on a Sabbath and told him to pick up his pallet and go home. It was enough that Jesus had told this man to break the Sabbath by picking up his pallet, but then he said some things that had angered some of the people.

Esclepius, like Dionysus, was half god and half human. He was raised by an earthly father who was a physician who loved Esclepius and showed him everything about healing. Esclepius loved his father and his father's calling, so when other boys were out playing, Esclepius was watching his father work and learning all he could. One day when his father was out, a man came to the clinic and Esclepius healed him, as his father would have. Esclepius went even further and raised a man from the dead. Because he had restored life, Esclepius was killed, but he came back to life and lived on to heal and raise others.[9] The day that Jesus healed the man by the shrine to Esclepius, the Judeans started pressuring Jesus about breaking the Sabbath, and Jesus started using Esclepius' language to refer to himself. "... the Son can do nothing on his own... only what he sees the Father doing... whatever the Father does, the Son does... the Father loves the Son and shows him all that he himself is doing... the Son does likewise...." (John 5:19-21)

He went on to say that he would raise people from the dead. He was teaching the people about himself by using the well-known Esclepius story—anyone who was there would have recognized it. It was Jesus' way of saying once again, "I am the One! You of God's people know that Esclepius, the god of this shrine, is not real. But I am!" Since Jesus was one of God's people, too, the implication was that he was the son of the creator God of the Hebrew people. He was equal to the one true God and could do anything that God could do, just as Esclepius could do anything that his father could do! So, first, Jesus had broken the Sabbath, and then in the same breath he had committed blasphemy in the eyes of those who did not know who he was! The Judeans, it was said, were infuriated!

When I had first heard this story, I had hoped against hope that it

---

9. On a similar note, the raising of Lazarus played a role in inciting the authorities to put Jesus to death (John 11:45-53), who likewise came back to life to heal and raise others.

was false. But it seemed too detailed not to be true. I had never advertised who Jesus' father was, and it seemed such a needlessly dangerous thing for him to do. Had Jesus lost sight of what his ministry was really about? At this rate, he would not be around long enough to teach anyone anything about what God really wanted from us. Had the pressure of his ministry become too great? Some people thought so! They were saying that Jesus was crazy, or that he had a demon. The demon I did not give a second thought, but had he lost touch with reality? Was he already losing touch that day we talked, and had I not picked up on it? Was I so hopeful for him, so enamored of my son, so wanting him to be and do right, that I had missed something that a mother should see? Maybe I should go to the place where he was teaching and see what was going on. Perhaps he needed me! I would go to him and get him to come home and rest for a while! That would be good for him. We could talk as we once did, and I could see for myself how he was.

I had tried to see him once already, but I had come home without finding him. Jesus had been around the area for a while, teaching and healing, using Capernaum as his home base. Word of the healings, in particular, had spread very quickly. Every person in the area with a disease, curable or incurable, was being brought to Jesus. I was neither aware of the numbers of people who were seeking healing, nor what it was like to be there with the crowds of people wanting help, until that day when I had gone to try to see Jesus and hear him teach. He was to have been in an open area near the sea, not far from home, and I thought that I could slip away by myself and observe what was happening. I was curious about the healings, but I thought that even if no one came to be healed, I could still hear him teach. I really wanted to hear him!

As I approached the area where Jesus was to be teaching that day, I was vaguely aware that people were coming toward him from all directions, but my thoughts were so focused on Jesus that I really did not look at the others or notice anything unusual about them. As I got closer, I realized that crowds of people were growing around me. I had strolled in, simply to hear my son speak and perhaps see a healing, but with those around me, there was a sense of desperation. I wondered briefly at people wanting to hear Jesus' teachings so badly, but I still was not really seeing them. I was intent only on seeing Jesus.

Time went quickly as I continued to make my way toward Jesus, and before I realized it was happening, the crowd had grown so thick that it was pressing in around me. It became obvious that I was not going to get any closer to Jesus, and I was rapidly growing indignant that I should have to struggle to hold my place to hear my own son speak! Obviously these people did not know who I was! I was actually thinking of calling out to Jesus, so that he would rescue me from this crowd and show these people that I was his mother. But before I could call out, I felt something wet against my hand, and I looked down. A chill engulfed my entire being as I saw, to my horror, that the arm pressing against me was a leper's arm. His bandage had been pulled away in the shuffling of this smothering crowd, and a seeping sore was pressing against the back of my hand! I recoiled in terror, but as I spun around, my only thought to escape, I lunged hard against the limp legs of a small child being held in her father's arms.

"Watch what you're doing!" snarled the father, but his voice only rang from the distance as, startled and shaken, I stood motionless, gazing into the lifeless eyes of a limp little girl. She seemed to be about five years old, and her pallid skin barely covered her skeleton. Tears flooded my eyes as I looked to the parents' faces. Even through my tears, I could see the last vestige of hope written in their eyes; a determination set in their jaws. Nothing on this earth would keep them from seeing my son.

As I gave way to them, moving in a direction away from Jesus, I allowed my eyes for the first time to roam over the crowd. Nearly in shock with what I had just seen, I was now shaken back to reality by the sight of the surrounding crowd. I was now seeing every malady of which I had ever heard. There were people flushed with fever, others missing limbs, some were malformed...and the children! Oh, the children grieved me. Some were leprous with oozing sores. Some limped with crutches, struggling to stay upright in the crowd. As my eyes fell on the crutches, I wondered fleetingly if my beloved Joseph, or even Jesus, had made them. In the days when they had fashioned tools in the shop, occasionally someone would come in wanting a crutch for a loved one. As my mind was leading me away, a child's seizure brought me back. Right next to me, he began to thrash as his parents struggled to hold him. Spittle flew and limbs flailed, but still people mercilessly crowded near, unwilling to give up their places. All had come seeking a healing, and they would stay as near to Jesus as they could.

Humbled once again, I allowed myself to be shuffled away from my son. The people around me had not come to hear Jesus' teaching, which could bring wholeness to them in soul and spirit; they had come only for physical healing, the least of the gifts that Jesus had to offer. I pressed on toward the back of the crowd, people grudgingly parting to let me by and as quickly filling the space I left behind. I reached the back of the crowd with a sense of relief at no longer being surrounded. I felt unclean from all that I had touched and seen—and I was flooded with sadness for my son. So lovingly had I protected my baby from that which now crowded in around him.

I realized now why, at times, Jesus had told those he healed not to tell anyone. The desire for physical healing was often so great that the way to spiritual healing was overshadowed. But even now in the midst of the growing urgency of this crowd, Jesus, in his compassion, would heal those that he could, before the crowd became too threatening. When that happened, he would get into a boat and push off from shore to keep from being crushed.

Freed from the pressures of the crowd, I became aware of the hot sun beating down upon my head. Growing faint, I headed in the direction of home. Perhaps I could hear Jesus teach another day.

As I walked, my mind raced. I tried not to think, for I could hardly stand the thought that my child—my little boy—whom I had protected and cared for, was there in the midst of that crowd of lepers and others whose only concern was physical well-being for themselves or for those whom they loved. I didn't want him there! He shouldn't be there! How could he risk exposing himself to so many diseases? Had he forgotten that he had a mission to accomplish? I was deeply troubled and wondered if Jesus had lost sight of what he was to be doing.[10]

Several days later, after roaming around Galilee calling upon disciples, teaching, and of course healing, Jesus came back home to Capernaum.[11] When I heard that he was back, I imagined that I would prepare his favorite food, and he would come over, and we would share a meal and talk. I thought about it so much, that even though I had not yet

10. There is no record that Mary actually went to see Jesus teach and heal, but since she was his mother, and he did teach in the area, I can hardly imagine her not venturing out to see him. This account considers what she might have found if she did go.

11. Jesus did come to Capernaum (Mark 3:19b-35). Again, I consider what Mary must have thought and done as his mother.

seen Jesus to ask him if he could come, my mind envisioned him already here. Then I heard that the crowds had followed him to the house where he and his disciples were staying. More people had then gathered, and the crowd's demands became so great that Jesus and his disciples could not even eat!

We had some family in Capernaum—cousins of Jesus[12]—so I talked it over with them, and we decided that enough was enough. Jesus had to come to his senses. People were saying outright that he was crazy—and who knew what else they were saying. We would go to him and bring him home for a rest—whether he wanted to come or not! We would send the crowds on their way and give Jesus and his disciples a much needed break.

We set out as soon as we had made the decision to help Jesus, and it didn't take us long to get to the area where Jesus and his disciples were staying. When the house came within sight, we could see that there were crowds packed all around it. It was going to be hard to get to Jesus, but we had decided what we were going to do, and we began to push our way through. As we struggled, threading our way through the crowd, the sense of urgency grew. It was as though the resistance of the crowd made us feel all the more strongly that we simply must get to Jesus.

Finally we got near enough to catch a glimpse of the people closest to the house. Some of the men were dressed differently than anyone else, and the crowd seemed to be watching them. As we got closer, it became obvious that they were scribes from Jerusalem, and that they were carrying on a conversation with Jesus, who was inside the house. But they were also talking to the crowd. We could not see Jesus, but we began to make out what was being said, and it was not good. The first voice we heard was that of a scribe speaking to the crowd so that Jesus could hear!

"He has Beelzebul, the leader of the forces of evil! How else could he cast out demons, unless he was on good terms with the prince of demons?"

At this, most of the crowd stood in shocked silence. They had come for healing or to hear teaching that would make a difference in their lives. They did not expect to hear that the one they followed was evil! But there were others who were pleased by what was said. They were the ones who thrived on dissension; who would take on any fight that came their way.

12. Cousins were called brothers and sisters in Bible times. Whether or not Mary and Joseph actually gave Jesus brothers and sisters is not certain. For the sake of narrative, I have arbitrarily chosen to assume that the "brothers" were cousins.

They had actually come, not for spiritual edification, but to see a sideshow, and they loved what they were hearing now! "Yeah! Let him explain that one!" they cried. "Hey, Jesus! You listening?!"

My blood turned cold with horror, when I heard what was happening. The whole situation suddenly seemed unreal. I had hoped, when I first saw the scribes, that they were learning from Jesus, and that the opinion of the religious officials was somehow being swayed. Now my hopes were dashed! I could not understand why these men would be saying such things! They must have had their reasons. These were reputable men. Surely they would not say these things for no reason at all. Was there something terribly wrong with my Jesus?! It seemed all the more urgent now to get him to come home with me and rest. As I was thinking these things, I heard Jesus responding to the accusation against him. With a voice steady and clear, and not at all the voice of a crazy man, he calmly told a story to illustrate that Satan would not be casting out his own spirits.

"A house divided cannot stand," he said, and suddenly I felt divided from him, as I realized that I had allowed others around me to touch my own inner doubts and sway me away from what I knew to be true. I wondered if our house—Joseph's and mine—could stand, because of my weaknesses, my readiness to be moved. Then, suddenly, I realized that these scribes, who claimed to be God's people did not have minds that were open to God's right to work in new ways. They would divide God's house by opposing this one who was God's son, and who was intent on doing God's will. I could hear anger in Jesus' voice and I knew that, whatever the scribes were thinking, Jesus considered them clearly out of line.

When he finished the parable, he tackled the scribes head on. I heard him say, "I tell you the truth, people will be forgiven for their sins and whatever blasphemies they utter; but whoever blasphemes against the Holy Spirit can never have forgiveness, but is guilty of an eternal sin." He was telling the scribes that it was unforgivable to stand there and look at him and believe that the Spirit in him was evil. To look at pure goodness and see treachery, to look at God and see the prince of demons, was the ultimate blasphemy! It was unforgivable, for it betrayed a self-righteous spirit that was perverted and hardened beyond hearing God's will.

When I heard Jesus' voice and the words that he spoke, that peace that I knew only in his presence began to settle over me, and something clicked inside me. Then I realized with horror what I had come to do. In my mind, suddenly I could hear him saying, "The way is going to get really rough now. Some of what I am going to do, you will not understand. Please remember the things we have talked about today when you doubt me—and try to trust."

What should I do? I struggled alone even as I was being jostled about by the crowd. I wanted to trust, but what if Jesus did need to go home and rest, and I found later that I had turned my back on him when he needed me most? But his voice sounded good. He seemed strong. My instinct was to trust him and simply go home.

As these thoughts were racing through my mind, the rest of the family was having second thoughts, too, but their concern was with the difficulty of trying to take Jesus away with the people crowding in. Many in the crowd would not take kindly to our trying to remove him. They wanted to hear Jesus and see him perform miracles and heal people. I looked at those who were with me. I could see the doubt in their eyes. I was about to suggest that we simply leave when one of our group poked someone standing ahead of us and said, "Pass the word to Jesus that his mother and the rest of his family are out here and want to see him." By this time I wished we hadn't come at all, but it was too late to turn back now, and surely Jesus would meet with us, if only to remind me, with his gentle voice and kind smile, that I must trust. That would be enough, and I did so want to see him and be reassured by him.

Then I heard someone closer to the front yell, "Hey, Jesus! Your family is here! From the looks of them, I'd say they want to drag you home!" That brought a huge roar of laughter from the skeptics in the crowd and caused quite a stir among the crowd in general. People began to crane their necks toward us. Some were curious to see what Jesus' mother looked like. Others were disgruntled that we would consider taking him home. Those who stood accusing Jesus looked at us with eyes of judgement and disgust.

Then Jesus' voice came from inside the house. "Who are my mother and the rest of my family?" I could hear sadness in his voice, but resolve as well, and I remembered that we had made a clean break the day of our last long conversation. Now I had let him down by not simply trusting. It was so hard to separate myself from him and let him do things his own way, but I knew I would not try to interfere again, no matter how things appeared from my point of view. "Here are my mother and family!" Jesus' voice broke clearly into my thoughts and my heart. "Whoever does the will of God is my family!"

I turned toward the back of the crowd and began to make my way out. He had told me how to be his mother; go home and trust. There were tears in my eyes again as I looked down to avoid the sympathetic looks as well as the chuckles and smirks. But these were not tears of rejection or sadness, as I'm sure others thought. They were the same tears that I had shed the day Jesus and I had said our goodbyes. Jesus loved me and knew that this would happen. That is why he had warned me. With a growing sense of peace settling in around old Simeon's sword in my soul, I made my way toward home.

CHAPTER 12

The Coronation Nears

I didn't see Jesus for quite some time after that. He was constantly traveling and, as time passed, he was in more and more danger because of the radicals who wanted to destroy him. These people, who were so outspoken and adamant about their "faith," tried spreading gossip and rumors about him, and left no question that if talk did not stop him, his death would be the next choice. They were certain that they were doing the right thing. Their hearts were hardened in a way that made it impossible for them to see that Jesus' way of gentleness and love and forgiveness was the right way. His way was vastly different from their way, which involved a hard, inflexible keeping of the Law.[1] For them, rules were rules, black was black, white was white, and there was no tempering their rules with love. It was as though they worshiped the Law itself, and felt they had to protect it and keep it undefiled. They wanted the Law kept for the Law's sake, not for the people's benefit. Oh, they were such hard and rigid people! It seemed that even God could not soften their hearts and open their eyes. They found their security not in God, but in being right, and therefore could not even consider that they might be wrong. I guess they all needed miracles like the one Jesus had worked on old blind Bartimaeus. After Jesus touched him, Bartimaeus could see—with his eyes. These people needed Jesus' touch so they could see with their hearts. They were in need of the deepest kind of healing. And sadly, there were common people who mistook the rigidness of these radicals for confidence and followed them blindly.

I could not handle the weight of the danger that Jesus faced, so,

---

1. Both the Sadducees (a political group made up of priests) and the Pharisees (a party of learned and zealous lay people which had arisen to challenge the spiritual authority of the corrupted priesthood) tended to be radical. The Sadducees were conservative and severe in their approach to God's laws! The Pharisees, who had dwindled to a minority by Jesus' time, were strict, but tended to be democratic, humane, and even progressive in their interpretation of the Law.

withdrawing from all that was around me, I shut myself away into my own little world. I would tend to my daily chores, trying in all that I did to live by the principles which Jesus taught, but I would avoid the stress that others were wont to place upon me. I would go to the well when the other women were not there, in order to miss all the free-flowing gossip. I would close my ears when rumors dripped from the lips of well-meaning friends who had come to visit. And when those people who thought Jesus was not doing right by me would go out of their way to tell me, I nodded and smiled, barely hearing what they said.

As people realized that I would not listen to them or gossip with them, one by one they quit coming. My life became lonely, as the lives of those who live only for a greater purpose often do. I kept busy, but when things would slow down too much, and my mind could no longer be kept from thoughts of Jesus, then I worried as a mother does, wondering if my son was safe. At those times, I would remind God that this was his son, too, as all children are his children. I was comforted by that thought and by the realization that God was with my son and loved him even more than I did. As I entrusted my son to God, I had peace once again. I knew that if God wanted me involved in Jesus' life, He would show me the way. It was a lesson that had taken me three years to learn—or maybe I should say, thirty-three!

Then one day, as I was missing my son terribly, something happened that made it easy for me to decide to get involved again. It was strange the way it came about, and reflecting on it, I am sure that it was God's way of getting me where I needed to be. I had settled down in Capernaum,[2] and Jesus would die in Jerusalem. God, who had given me this Jesus as a baby, knew that I would need to be there when he died. God uses unlikely people to accomplish what needs to be done, even people who do not believe, or those who say they believe, but make little or no attempt to follow the ways of God. In this case it was the last person I ever would have guessed, who brought God's message to me.

I was going to the well to fetch some water early one Tuesday

2. Mary lived in Capernaum, and likely did not accompany Jesus on his journeys, but was at the foot of the cross. I have chosen a fictitious character, Matthias, which means *gift of God*, to get her where she needed to be. He takes her to Martha's house, where we imagine what might have happened. Finally Mary reaches the foot of the cross and then resumes being found in the places where the Biblical narrative places her.

morning, when a young man came galloping into town on a horse.[3] I was alone on a narrow street when I realized that this rider was bearing down on me with great speed. People had begun to peer out their windows and were stepping into their front yards when the rider reigned his horse in sharply—not two feet from where I stood. Startled, I pressed my back to the wall that bordered the street. My water jug fell from my head and crashed to the ground, breaking as it hit. It was the same jug that my mother had sent to the well with me when I was a child, and it held many memories. My temper flared, blurring the potential danger. I was angry! Why was this soldier targeting me, pinning me against the wall with his spirited horse? The horse snorted and hit the ground hard with his hoof, almost as though he were saying, "Pay attention!"

My mind raced. Was this Roman soldier looking for a woman to use and discard?! And here I was alone! Or was he weary of being away from home, angry with a nation that kept him from his family for years at a time, and looking for someone of whom he could make an example— on whom he could vent his frustrations? My heart pounded loudly in my ears, blocking out other sounds.

Or had this man possibly stopped me because… I was Jesus' mother? Was Jesus in trouble, and was I to be imprisoned with him? Thoughts tumbled through my mind and my emotions followed—fear replacing anger, anger replacing fear! Gathering back my courage, I raised my eyes slowly to see what the rider might have to say to me. As my eyes reached the level of his feet, I saw the sandals of a common man—not a soldier. Raising my sight more quickly now, my eyes confirmed that this man was indeed not a soldier! He wore the light colored robe of a Hebrew from the north! Fixing my gaze on this intruder's face, I recognized with rising anger, the mocking grin of a man I knew—Matthias!

Matthias had grown up with Jesus, and evidently, he had not changed from the irritating soul he had always been. How dare he frighten me this way! But how like him! I knew that the anger that flashed hot in my eyes only added to Matthias' glee. He was apparently very satisfied

---

3. God's people did not own horses, since in that land where food was not plentiful, feeding horses (which eat a lot) would mean taking food from people. Horses were a symbol of power, and owning them was sinful—an indication of taking power into one's own hands instead of trusting God. When the Bible mentions ownership of horses (e.g. Solomon) it is telling us something is not right. (Donkeys were more suited than horses to the hill country in which God's people lived, because they were smaller, more nimble, and ate less.)

with himself and seemed to think he could risk my anger. He had always been one of those boys that makes a mother feel uneasy—so polite, so respectful, so smiling when adults are around, that he aroused suspicion. Matthias was the kind who would cheerfully get some sort of trouble going, involve other boys, and then draw back and watch with a smirk when the others got caught and paid the price. He was also the sort who could bribe a stable guard into letting him borrow a Roman horse when he had a piece of juicy information to deliver somewhere. I never liked Jesus to play with Matthias, but when I would object, Jesus would tell me in that child's voice—that I now loved remembering—that I, myself, had taught him right from wrong. He told me that I had encouraged him not to exclude those children who were not fortunate enough to have someone to teach them, but rather to play with them and show them the right way. Matthias never seemed to catch on, though, and I had long since decided that our efforts with him were wasted.

When Jesus began his ministry, Matthias was still around—still too polite—still on the fringes of the action—present, but not involved, ready to be a part of glory if it came, or ready to be a part of the opposition if plans went awry. Now, here he was again, satisfied with himself for having frightened me half to death! When my eyes reached his face, his grin grew into a look of triumph. Well, Matthias was still Matthias, and one could only accept him. He was, after all, a piece of God's handiwork, and angry as I was that day, I will always be grateful for his coming.

In a comradely voice, as though we had always been the closest of friends, he said, "I came as quickly as I could! I knew you'd want to know. Jesus has declared his kingship! If you hurry, you should be able to get to Jerusalem in time to see him enthroned!" I stood there, my mouth open but silent, looking at this man from whose mouth the truth had seldom come. And in a moment of weakness, weary of my loneliness and worry, longing for some flicker of hope—I believed what he was telling me! I wanted to believe him! I had had enough of Simeon's sword! What he was saying meant that the struggle was over! Now it would be Mary, Mother of the King! Jesus on a throne to which he had a right! The whole world under his rule! Peace for all! And with my loneliness at an end—a place of honor awaited me at his side!

Tears of relief filled my eyes, and Matthias, seeing that I believed him, was encouraged and quickly took charge. "Go home! Gather your things! And waste no time about it!" he said. "We must be on our way!" I turned, and leaving my broken water jug in the street, I hurried home. I didn't know how homesick I had been for Jesus until I realized I was going to see him—perhaps be reunited with him, to live the rest of my life in his home! I felt within me an urgency about getting to Jesus' side, and that sense of urgency helped me fight a feeling deep in the pit of my stomach that what I was hearing was not exactly true. No doubt, what Matthias was describing was fact, but would the outcome be what he expected? I wanted to believe Matthias. I wanted to see Jesus. Matthias' arrival had loosed the longings for my son that I had reined in so tightly. Now that those long-ings were set free, I would not listen to my own nagging doubts. I would not listen to my own good sense! I was going to Jerusalem—quickly!

Matthias rode the horse alongside me as I headed home. "This is Tuesday," he said. "It's still early. If we leave soon, we should be there by late Thursday." When I reached my home and started inside, Matthias dis-mounted and followed me.

"Keep it light!" he ordered. "We have to travel fast." My mistrust and dislike of this man welled up in me again. With him standing there watching, I found it hard to think of what I needed for the trip. He was still the same self-centered child I had known. He was just playing bigger games now.

I gathered my things together in haste as the wagging tongues of neighbors who had followed me into the house sang congratulations. These same tongues had been my companions during the long, lonely months of mulling over the whereabouts of my son. Then they were only too willing to carry to me all the chilling rumors about Jesus—the worse the rumors were, the more worthy of repeating, they seemed to think. They would justify their gossip with, "Just thought you would want to know, his being your son and all." I had ignored them then, and now I accepted their congratulations, but I did not slow down to listen to their "I always knew that boy would amount to something!" and "Don't forget your poor old friends here when you're living in luxury in Jerusalem!"

It was still fairly early on Tuesday when Matthias and I attached to a caravan that was leaving for the south. It was the week of Passover, which had fallen late this year, and since the barley harvest had come in early, more than the usual number of northern people were heading to

Jerusalem for the celebration. Contrary to what the southerners thought, we people from the north cherished an opportunity to get to the Holy City on holidays, especially Passover.[4] We were not the pagans we were accused of being. It was a simple matter of economics. When there was ripe grain in the field, farmers simply could not get away. Now, this year, in the midst of all the southern celebrants, a northerner would assume his throne and restore the kingdom as God intended it to be. I relished that thought, but I knew it would not be that simple. Jesus had said that he must die, and I had had a long, lonely time during which I had tried to learn to trust that what he said was true.

I quickly found old friends that I could walk with, but Matthias stuck close, walking beside me and leading his horse. He was anxious to tell me the whole story, but had saved it until we had started our journey, since any delay would increase the possibility of missing Jesus' greatest hour. Once we had begun our long walk, the whole story spilled out very quickly. I knew that Matthias was not the friend of Jesus' that he claimed to be, but I listened closely to him, trying to sort out the truth for myself.

He began by telling me that Jesus had really stirred people by restoring life to a man who had been dead and in his tomb for four days. According to Matthias, Jesus had deliberately stayed away from the little village of Bethany where his friend Lazarus was desperately ill. The family had sent for Jesus, who was in the other Bethany across the Jordan River. If the messenger had left first thing in the morning, he could have reached Jesus by ten o'clock and had him back to the family by four. Instead, Jesus received the message, but then lingered where he was, until Lazarus died. Only then did Jesus go—very slowly—to the family, arriving on the fourth day after Lazarus' death. Matthias threw a smirk my way, as though he especially enjoyed Jesus' putting off the family. The relatives were understandably upset when Jesus did arrive, because they knew Jesus could have healed their brother if he had come sooner.

Matthias enjoyed this part of the story so much that he grinned from ear to ear while walking and watching the road. But, that poor family! I knew them and I knew that they were among Jesus' closest friends.

---

4. Southerners looked down on Northerners, who seldom could get to Jerusalem to celebrate Passover, because the holiday came at a time when the barley was ready to harvest. Likewise, Pentecost fell at wheat harvest, preventing Northerners from making the pilgrimage to Jerusalem.

I was aghast, but Matthias was still chattering on, very proud of himself for bringing me this word. I looked at him in disgust, and then, disliking my own attitude, I let my eyes fall on the road again as we continued walking. Matthias was simply being Matthias, and without so much as an inkling of my reaction, he went on to tell how Jesus had surprised the family by bringing Lazarus back to life!

Matthias paused here in the story to relish what seemed like a cruel joke. He looked at me to see if he had made an impact. I did my best to ignore his gaze. I was sure that Jesus had had a good reason for what he did, or he would not have risked hurting his friends so badly. What I did not realize, until nearly a week later, was that Jesus was trying to prepare all those who loved him for his own death. He was showing us ahead of time that he ruled—even over death! And that rule extended to his own death as well as to the death of others. I wanted desperately to hear what Matthias had to say, and I hoped I would not have to look at him to get him started talking again. I didn't! What Matthias had to say was too good to hold in for long!

He continued. It seemed that Lazarus had been in the tomb four days when Jesus ordered the rock that sealed the entrance to the cave removed. Jesus had waited until the fourth day deliberately, because the life of a person lingers in the body until the third day, and only then are they truly dead.[5] But the people were aghast at his order! In that hot desert climate, a body begins to smell within an hour of two of death. It is for that reason that the body is coated with spices and incense, wrapped and placed in a sealed tomb in an attempt to contain the odor. By the fourth day after death, the body is in such bad shape that no one wants to breathe the air that would come from the tomb if someone broke the seal. So the professional mourners[6] that Mary and Martha had hired to come and bewail their brother had held their noses and covered their mouths when the seal was broken and the stone plug pulled out of the hole that was the only entrance to the tomb. Then Jesus had cried, "Come out of there, Lazarus!" and Lazarus had come—wrapped in grave cloths like a mummy, wriggling out of the small opening[7] through which the body had been put

5. A common belief in Jesus' time.
6. Families who could, hired professional mourners to weep and wail and show how grieved the family was. The family was expected to behave in a similar manner, showing their love for the deceased.

into the tomb, and then trying to stand, all bound up as a mummy, arms crossed on his chest, legs bound together. I could imagine the look on the faces of Mary and Martha. We believed that spirits—demons of a sort—roamed about, looking for bodies to inhabit. And spirits especially liked living in graveyards, hoping for a dead body to claim, so the two sisters, along with the rest of the crowd, probably thought they were seeing a possessed body. I chuckled anxiously at the thought, which Matthias took as a sharing in his attitude toward the whole thing. Feeling a sense of camaraderie, he drew closer to me as he went on.

"I was there when it happened," said Matthias, "so I know it's true! There were a lot of other people there, too, and they went off and told others. Especially those professional mourners! They kept telling people that they had seen a lot of death, but they had never seen anything like this!" Matthias' voice was becoming high pitched with excitement. It was obvious that he believed every word that he was saying. He continued, "Before long, crowds were looking for Jesus everywhere. He could bring the dead back to life, and they wanted to see him. Some just wanted him to bring back some of their family's members. Others were saying that even the Romans could not defeat someone who could control death. It makes a lot of sense, you know!" He looked at me to see how I was taking all this. Apparently he was encouraged, because he went on to tell me that, consequently, crowds were assured, when Jesus mounted the foal of a donkey and rode from Bethany into Jerusalem a week later.

"This was the moment we had all been waiting for," said Matthias, and he droned on, including himself as one of Jesus' disciples, speaking of his high expectations that when the time arrived, they would all help Jesus rule. As he went on, I took time out from listening to wonder if anyone, Matthias included, had noticed that Jesus didn't ride a horse—the symbol of power and military might that would be expected of a new ruler—but rather a donkey, the animal of the poor and powerless, used in times of peace. There was just a flicker of doubt about the accuracy of Matthias' prediction of where all this was heading. Then tuning in once again to what he was saying, I heard of people throwing their clothes on

---

7. Some graves in Palestine had only small low square openings going into them, so that they could be sealed better and prevent stench. One would need to slide the body in, and then creep through the opening to place the body on the stone shelf. When the burial was complete, the opening was plugged with a square stone, instead of having a stone slide or roll in front of it. John portrays this type of tomb with Lazarus and with Jesus.

the rocky road in front of Jesus in order to cushion the rough ride of the donkey. Others had gone off into private gardens and pilfered some palm branches[8]—the symbol of independence, control, and that which holds back evil. These they waved to show that they could hold back Rome, they could control, they could have power and freedom—for they had Jesus, who reigned over death. All the while, the crowds cheered Jesus on.

I listened to the rest of Matthias' story just to try to get some idea of what had actually happened. I kept having that feeling that all was not as simple as Matthias believed it to be. Still, I wanted to believe, with Matthias, that things were on the way up. It was obvious that he had come for me so he could improve his standing with Jesus, but I was grateful. In spite of my doubts concerning Matthias' prediction of enthronement, I felt certain that going to Jerusalem was the right thing for me to do. Somehow God would let me know if I was on the wrong track.

When Matthias finished his story, he began to move throughout the caravan, telling any who would listen about his experiences with Jesus. My friends had drifted off while Matthias was talking, so now I was left to walk alone with my thoughts. I mulled over the things he had said. As soon as Jesus had ridden into Jerusalem on Sunday, Matthias had left for Capernaum. Leaving immediately, he thought, would give him time to get me and still return to Jerusalem in time for Jesus' big moment. I thought with a soft cheerless chuckle, that coming for me also gave this rascal a chance to get out of town for a few days in case things did not go well and the axe fell on Jesus and his followers. No doubt people were upset by Jesus' declaration of his kingship and there was danger, but it would all be set straight when Jesus established himself on his throne. If what Matthias said was true, and I made myself believe that it was, this could be the greatest Passover since the very first one when God had delivered us from bondage. With the doubts pushed away once again, I walked quickly with renewed energy, hoping to arrive at our destination in time to be a part of Jesus' ascension to his throne. This would be the reward for my years of dedication and loneliness.

---

8. Palm trees were not native, but rather cultivated.

CHAPTER 13

Bethany

It was late Thursday when we neared Jerusalem. Matthias and I left the caravan at Bethany, a mile and a quarter out of the city, and went to the home of Mary and Martha in the hopes that Jesus was there. The women welcomed us warmly, although a brief glance between them spoke of their surprise at seeing Matthias and me together. "Is Jesus here?" I asked, barely taking time for pleasantries. It had been such a long time since I had seen my son, and I was growing quite anxious. Even as I spoke, I imagined his voice calling out, "Mother!" and his coming out of the house and gathering me in a warm embrace.

"No …," said Mary, hesitating, "but come in and we'll talk. I don't think you'll be able to find him this evening." Having invited us in, the women bade the slaves bring water and wash our feet and prepare food for us. It felt so good to sit down and have my weary feet cared for. I was too tired to be embarrassed, so I just relaxed and enjoyed.[1]

When our feet had been dried and rubbed with oil, we entered the comfort of the home of these wealthy friends, who were so kind and obviously loved Jesus very much. Then food was brought. I had not realized how hungry I was until I ate that first bite. Then I was suddenly ravenous and became so absorbed with the food that I was aware of little else.

As my hunger and thirst were satisfied, I began to relax. Only then did I notice Lazarus' presence. He had come into the room while I was eating and was watching me quietly. When I looked at him, he smiled tenderly. My gaze drifted to Mary and Martha, and I recognized a look of genuine concern on all their faces. They, in turn, recognized that I was ready to hear whatever they had to say.

1. In a land where people walked and wore sandals, a good host saw that his/her guests' feet were washed and anointed with oil to prevent drying and cracking. However, the feet were private—on a level with genitalia (for which foot is a euphemism in the Bible)—and could be touched only by someone with whom one was intimate or by the lowest of slaves who was not really a person at all. People normally cared for their own feet.

As Lazarus began to speak, my stomach tightened in fear. It was as though all those doubts I had controlled and suppressed as I had trudged along the road these past three days were now pushing out and expressing themselves. I was beginning to admit to myself that this was not to be simply a time of glorious coronation and celebration. Deep down, I knew that something terrible was going to happen. I listened intently.

"I suppose you've heard about my death, how Jesus brought me back to life, and then, how Jesus rode into Jerusalem accompanied by a crowd last Sunday," he asked, looking at me frankly. My head barely nodded. I wanted desperately to hear what else had happened, but I was so frightened that I wanted to know everything at once, before I lost my courage and tried to suppress the truth once again. I hoped he would not repeat what I had already heard—at least not now.

"Shortly after Jesus made his entrance into Jerusalem, we realized that Matthias had disappeared," he continued. "We had no idea that he had gone to get you—nor did Jesus. I doubt that he will be pleased." He shot a stern glance at Matthias, who avoided Lazarus' eyes. Coming to get me was a long shot that Matthias hoped would pay huge rewards.

"Jerusalem is not safe right now, and it would be better if you were back in Capernaum. But you're here, so I will bring you up to date on what has been happening." I nodded again, struggling to keep my mind from racing back and forth between hope and terror. Why would Jesus object to my presence if he were to be enthroned? The answer was obvious. His would not be a simple, glorious enthronement. I tried not to think about it, but I needed to face the truth. As I struggled, a terrible coldness slowly filled my body.

Lazarus went on. "Jesus has been spending his nights here with us since his ride into the city last Sunday, but he's been going into the temple to teach every day. I've not been going in with him, since there are some who would like to see me dead again. But Mary has been going, along with several others, and with Jesus here in the evenings, we're aware of most of what's been happening." Lazarus took a deep breath. I made a conscious effort to do the same.

"On Monday Jesus went into the temple, upset the tables of the money changers, and drove out the sellers with a whip! From that alone you can tell that things have not been quiet."

"Yes," I muttered, managing to move my chilled body a bit. I knew how strongly Jesus had always felt about those people who tried to get rich off the ones who came to worship; yet I could hardly imagine him with a whip! He was such a gentle boy! I smiled as I remembered times long past. It was so easy, so safe to let my mind wander in the past, where I was involved in my son's life; essential to him—in control! But he was a man now, and I needed to let him go. It might have been easier if I had been involved with him in his ministry, if I had been risking my life alongside him, instead of helplessly waiting to see what would happen. But I knew that Jesus was right in leaving me in Capernaum and asking me to simply trust him. And I had trusted, and it was good training for what was happening now, but I was always tempted to ask, "What if ..." and to try to second guess my Lord. It took some self-discipline to bring myself back to accepting the life that had been given me to live and recognizing that Jesus knew what he needed to do. Clearing my mind, I thought about the situation. What Jesus had done with the businessmen in the temple was sure to have angered many people. An entire economy thrived on the business he had attacked, and besides, the temple officials were very possessive about their area of authority and were easily incited by anyone who interfered or infringed in any way.

"But that's not all he did," Martha broke into my thoughts with an inquiring look on her face. I was not used to having people stop their conversation when my mind drifted off. These people were so kind! Seeing she had my attention, Martha went on gently.

"Jesus didn't stop that day with the money changers and sellers." She smiled when I looked alarmed. "He had a bunch of children there. You know how they gravitate toward him." She paused and her eyes looked warm.

"Mary convinced me to go into the city with her that day. I was glad I did, although one day was enough for me." She smiled. I knew what a homebody she was.

"When the turmoil had settled, people who were blind and lame came near, and of course, Jesus healed them." She paused again and I smiled, my throat aching and thickening, my eyes filled with tears. I was so proud of my son. I swallowed with difficulty and nodded.

"Being in Jesus' presence, seeing people healed and children happy—it's hard to describe, but it was like we were in the middle of a small peaceful kingdom apart from the violence that surrounded us—even though there had just been violence in that very room. There was a shared feeling that was… well… the kind of feeling you never want to end." Her face glowed.

"Then the children started singing just as they had at the parade on Sunday. Jesus was delighted and was having a good time with them when the chief priests and scribes came storming in. They were incensed that Jesus was allowing the children to sing to him as though he were the Messiah! They demanded he make the children be silent, but Jesus quietly defied them and the singing continued.

"Then it was time to leave, but, reluctant to go our separate ways, we all came back here.[2] The children played with Jesus and the adults watched. The servants quickly prepared some food for everyone, and we just … were together. It was a light-hearted evening. But it grew late and finally everyone left. Then Jesus leaned back and talked about the day. He told us how good it felt to drive those thieves out and how much fun he had had with the children."

Martha stopped here to let me digest all that she had said. I thought about the children. How he loved them! But my thoughts refused to stay with the children even though I tried to force them to do so. The cold fear was growing within me. Something was not right.

"He's in danger, isn't he?" I asked, hoping for a no, but knowing better.

"Every day they are looking for ways to kill him," said Lazarus, eyeing me sadly. I knew instinctively that if these people could make things better for me they would, but there was no denying the truth.

"He's been teaching openly this whole week," said Mary, "and those who oppose him have been growing more and more angry with each day." Mary was watching me closely.

"I'm fine," I murmured. I was fighting the weakness and the cold fear that threatened me. I could not allow my feelings to overcome me. What I wanted more than anything was to be near my son, so I must be prepared and able to endure the worst. Then I remembered, once again, that God is my strength and would see me through. For many years I had worked hard at trying to be God's obedient slave. That had given me a reservoir of strength to draw on, and now I would need it. I was deter-

---

2. Jesus spent time with the children in the temple. Everyone going to Mary and Martha's house afterward is fiction.

mined that whatever happened, I would be there for my son. Remembering that God had never failed me, I felt stronger.

Mary continued. "With the extra legions of Roman soldiers who have been brought in to keep order during Passover, the Judeans have to be very careful what they do to stop Jesus. The Passover crowds have been swelling all week long, and the Roman authorities are watching closely as more and more people flock to hear what Jesus has to say. A number of us are afraid that if the Pharisees and their cohorts don't put an end to Jesus, the Roman soldiers may. And if Rome does it, a lot of people will be hurt or even killed in the process. Those soldiers are always so afraid that we, as a people, might break into open rebellion at Passover[3]—especially if there is someone like Jesus that people just naturally follow. With our history they have a right to worry. Passover always seems to stir our longings for freedom, and it does increase the possibility of some of our people making a move against Rome."

Mary grew silent and reflective. It was obvious that this family was struggling to understand what Jesus was doing. If it was safety or earthly power that he wanted, it seemed to them that Jesus should either make his play or get out of town. I certainly could not disagree. The Romans were always very much aware of us, because, small insignificant nation that we were, we were always a potential trouble spot in the empire. Unlike other nations, we refused to give up our religion and accept Caesar as one of the gods. But it was not just that we would not worship Caesar and insisted on worshiping our own God in our own way; the religious zealots in Jerusalem and the surrounding countryside were quite volatile and made rebellion a constant possibility. As a people, we would try to get along with Rome as well as we could, so long as we could keep worshiping God, but the zealots would push things to the extreme and rebel openly if they even suspected that anyone was considering making us do otherwise. Beyond that they expected Rome to respect—not just tolerate—but respect our ways in Jerusalem. For example, if Roman guards came into Jerusalem bearing standards with a likeness of Caesar, the zealots would consider that an insult to God because it was bringing an 'image' near the temple of God. At any infraction of our religious commandments—real or perceived—the

---

3. This was a genuine concern of Rome.

zealots were ready to demonstrate, putting the lives of men, women, and children on the line. And they did not hesitate at the thought that all might die! Better to die than to have their beliefs defiled! There was no compromise with them. Pilate had found himself in a difficult position more than once. I believe he really was a man who wanted to keep the peace and be fair, but it was necessary that his actions leave no doubt that Rome ruled. If the zealots threatened a demonstration or actually staged one, and Pilate gave in, then they would just go one step further, rebelling again to get more of their own way. If there was open rebellion, the emperor would have Pilate's head. If, on the other hand, Pilate got tough and had the demonstrators slaughtered or let them starve themselves, the emperor would have Pilate's head for losing so many tax-paying subjects. It was a near no-win situation, and Pilate walked a fine line. He seemed a decent man, and I could not help but feel sorry for him at times.

Lazarus cleared his throat. I looked at him and tried a weak smile. I really was feeling more at peace since I had remembered that my strength was in God and my place was simply to be there for Jesus no matter what happened. Lazarus returned a solemn smile of encouragement and spoke. "Caiaphas was heard saying that it would be better for one man to die for the people than to have the whole nation destroyed. I know he meant Jesus, and at this point, it doesn't matter to him whether Jesus is right in what he teaches or not. As High Priest, Caiaphas is concerned that if Jesus doesn't die now, a lot of other people will die with him when the Roman soldiers attack the masses who are gathering around Jesus. So you see, it's not just a matter of Jesus usurping their power. It's a matter of protecting the people from the cruelty of the Romans, as well. It takes a lot of faith to trust God for protection, instead of trusting our own schemes! And right now, Caiaphas is responsible, and he's not willing to entrust his responsibility into anyone else's hands, not even if those hands belong to God. In his eyes, Jesus must die."

Lazarus smiled at me kindly, a shallow, joyless grin that spoke of the irony of the situation. So long we had waited for the Messiah to come to save the people, and now that he was here, the religious leaders would have him killed in an attempt to save the same people. I returned a worried look. I could understand Caiaphas' dilemma. Rome would likely attempt to arrest Jesus in order to make an example of him. And slaughtering any who got in their way would once again send a message from

Rome that insurrection would be dealt with viciously. A people who insisted on worshiping the one true God instead of the Roman gods and Caesar—who, even on the threat of death, decisively and openly defied any order they thought might be offensive to their God—and who had openly rebelled on more than one occasion in the past, were a people who, in Rome's eyes, were constantly in need of a message. It was a message the soldiers were wont to send. Here was Jesus, teaching openly, allowing the crowds to gather, not even trying to hide himself.

Caiaphas saw himself in a tough spot. Unlike some of the Romans who actually saw Jesus as a help in handling this difficult people, Caiaphas did not seem to know that Jesus did not teach open rebellion, or rebellion at all! Jesus said that if a soldier forced you to carry his gear one mile, as he could by law, you should go beyond the requirement and carry it two miles. He said not to resist evil, and to return good for evil, and to pray for your enemies and those who persecuted you. Suddenly it hit me that however Jesus planned to establish himself, it would not be by military might. What could he be thinking? How I wished I could be at that meeting with him and his men this evening. In a way, I understood Caiaphas. I struggled, too. As Jesus' mother, I did not want to see Jesus die any more than Caiaphas wanted to see thousands of Judeans die. I had long recognized that death was likely the direction in which Jesus was headed. My natural desire was to get him out of town somewhere where he would be safe, even though I knew that what he was doing was right. Unlike Caiaphas, I would put my trust completely in God! If Jesus must die, so be it. I, his mother, would be there at his side, no matter what.

Jesus was in more immediate danger than I had imagined, and I had heard as much about it as I could handle that night. The trip down from Capernaum had taken its toll. I just could not listen to anymore tonight. I wanted to see my Jesus. My throat tightened and ached again, and the seeds of tears formed in my eyes and threatened to grow. Let the tears come if they would, one thing I knew; whatever would happen would happen, but I would be near him!

The talking had continued in spite of my obvious uneasiness. I guess my host and hostess felt they could not stop talking when things sounded so negative. Now they were telling me something about Jesus needing to move quickly to establish himself or go somewhere where he would be safe. I think it was Martha who was taking a turn, but my mind was elsewhere. Instinct told me that the Simeon's sword of the past was nothing compared to what I was about to feel. The next few days, I knew, would be either days of great joy—or great sorrow. I was not sure which, but I was beginning to believe it would be sorrow that would reign. But then, with Martha's voice droning on in the background, I remembered Jesus' gentle voice—but it was more than remembering, it was almost as though I were actually hearing it again. Maybe I was, or maybe I was exhausted and had heard too much, but it was there:

"Some of the things that I am going to have to do, you will not understand. Please remember what we've talked about and try to trust." I could see once again his sad eyes pleading with me, and I resolved to trust, no matter what; strengthened again, I returned to the conversation at hand. Little did I know how much that trust would be tried.

Lazarus was talking again. "I don't know where Jesus and his disciples are this evening. I heard Jesus tell the others that they should go and prepare a room where they would gather this evening and celebrate Passover tomorrow. When the disciples asked what room they should use, Jesus told them to go into the city and follow a man carrying a jar of water." If the situation hadn't been so serious, this would have been a funny thought. I looked up at Lazarus. He paused, happy to see that I was listening. The water jug had caught my attention, as he thought it might. Carrying water is a woman's job. That man would certainly not be difficult to spot!

Lazarus continued. "When they followed him, he would take them to the upstairs guest room that they were to use." I nodded. Some people built rooms on the tops of their houses simply to use as guest rooms. During Passover, visitors in Jerusalem would rent such rooms for their Passover meals, which were always eaten within the city walls.

Lazarus was still talking. "It was obvious to me that Jesus didn't want anyone to know where he would be. But I can understand that. With a price on his head, he needs some time alone with those closest to him before he establishes his throne." At this, Lazarus seemed to slip off into his own thoughts. I looked at him with sympathy, as I saw signs of regret on his face. In some ways, I guess he would have liked to have been included among those closest to Jesus, but he understood. The key role that he was to play had already been accomplished, and now he must be content to stand back and allow the others to have their turn. Besides, there were those who were out to take Lazarus' life because of the role that he had played and his presence would only add danger to an already volatile situation.

About this time, Matthias shifted in his seat and knocked over the goblet from which he had been sipping water. I started and my head jerked in his direction. I had completely forgotten that he was there! At a glance, I could see that he, too, would have liked to have been a part of Jesus' private meeting. When he made his decision to fetch me, he ran the risk of being left out of things like that. A smile flickered in my heart. He also ran the risk of missing out on the danger involved. That was the sort of risk that Matthias would be willing to take.

Martha was talking now. I turned back to her as a servant wiped up the water that Matthias had spilled. "I think Jesus needs to be alone with his key men so he can explain his strategy to them and let them know what he's going to need from them when he takes over. And of course they need to celebrate that 'the hour' has finally arrived after all those months and years they spent on the road."

'The hour' threw me back to the wedding at Cana. "My hour has not yet come," he had said. Now it was here. It seemed so long ago, and yet such a short time.

"I'm thankful I didn't have to travel with them that whole time!" Martha was still talking.

Mary shifted her weight and prepared to speak. She and her sister were so different! I was sure Mary would have liked to have been with Jesus throughout his ministry. For her, roughing it on the road would have been worth the inconvenience, if it meant learning from Jesus. Martha was content to stay at home and have others tell her what was happening. She loved providing for Jesus when he was in the area. Always a gracious hostess, she opened her home to him, gladly feeding and sheltering him and his friends, no matter how many there were. She saw such things as a woman's natural role and was quite impatient when Mary did not act accordingly.

Mary had no desire to manage a home. She had always been more interested in learning the Law and the Prophets than any woman was supposed to be in our culture. If Jesus was near, she would go out seeking him. And if he was in their home, Mary wanted to be with the men, listening and learning instead of serving, as a woman ought—at least according to Martha and our culture. They were so different, it was amazing that they were sisters—and Jesus loved them both deeply! He always wanted people to be whatever God had created them to be, and that was different for each person.

The conversation continued with Mary speaking. She was more than ready to explain the significance of this particular evening. "Do you realize that this is the eve of Passover?" she asked. "Tomorrow we celebrate our deliverance from Egypt." She sat thinking for a moment, staring at her lap, then reflectively, without looking up, "So many years ago, God brought us out of slavery back to this land of our ancestors, where we could be free. Now tonight, God prepares a small group of people and their leader to deliver us once again." She was quiet for a bit, but obviously not finished. Then, "After this year, Passover will have a double meaning. As the angel of death passed over our people..." She looked up. Her eyes found Lazarus and rested on him as the light of a new thought grew brighter on her face. She looked at me. "I've been thinking only of freedom from Rome..." she said with wonder. "Oh, Mother of Jesus, this is going to be even greater than our deliverance from Egypt..." Her mind was still working, putting things together. "John said Jesus was the lamb who takes away the sins of the world. And we know that death came into the world through sin." Her eyes returned to Lazarus for a time. Then she looked at me, the look on her face inquiring if I understood. Her eyes dropped to the floor as she pulled within herself to contemplate her new thought. "Could it be?" she asked quietly of herself. I sat silently, no words wanting to come to my lips. All I could do was gaze at her with wonder. I wondered not only at her thoughts, but at her! What a change Jesus had wrought in this lovely creature when he had encouraged her to break with the mores of the day and learn from him, a rabbi, about God's ways—in spite of the fact that she was a woman. Now here she was, absolutely confident that tomorrow was the day—Jesus' day—and it would be a day of triumph such as the world had never seen. "I can't explain what's going to happen," she spoke once again, "but I know that it will be great beyond our wildest dreams, and the freedom we receive will be much more than we have hoped for!" Standing, she came toward me. I rose to meet her and we fell into one another's arms. We hugged and wept for joy and for sorrow. I had no idea how Jesus was going to accomplish what he needed to do, but like Mary, I knew he would somehow, and I was sure that tomorrow would be the day!

CHAPTER 14

Jerusalem

Fatigue from the long days of walking was tugging on my eyelids by now, and my body was longing to lie down. Martha, the gracious hostess, was quick to recognize my needs and suggested we all retire early. "After all," she said, "tomorrow will be a long day, and we all need our rest." Turning to me, she spoke tenderly, "Mother of Jesus, I know your heart is set on going into Jerusalem tomorrow, but they say the population has gone from twenty thousand to about one hundred thousand for the Passover this year and the crowds are terrible. You are not as young as you once were, and I could not possibly allow you to go into the city alone."

Matthias shifted in his chair, scraping his feet on the floor and clearing his throat loudly. Martha knew Matthias, and glancing briefly at him, she continued. "Having Lazarus go with you is not an option, since there is danger whenever he leaves this house. I think it would be best if you stayed here with us. Jesus' followers know our situation, and they will keep us informed of what is happening."

At this, Matthias stood up, and glancing at him, I answered Martha quickly. "My dear friend," I said as kindly and diplomatically as I could, "I have come all this way to see my son, and I appreciate your hospitality and your concern, but I will be going into Jerusalem tomorrow. I plan to leave just before first light, so that I will be there in time to see whatever happens."

"I will be going with her," offered Mary. Poor practical Martha's face flashed with anger. She knew in her own mind how things "ought" to be, and she often clashed with this liberal spirited, spiritual sister of hers, who did not hesitate to speak her own mind.

"Besides," added Mary, "Matthias will be with us." Matthias smirked, and Martha simply set her jaw and gave Mary a stern stare.

Lazarus stood up. "There will be dangerous situations to deal with tomorrow. You both know that?" he queried with a concerned glance at each of us. Mary and I both nodded and Lazarus returned a nod of understanding. "Then, we had better all get some rest," he said. "Martha, will you show the Mother of Jesus to the guest room? Matthias can sleep with the servants." Having finalized things, he led Matthias away, and I followed Martha.

Never had stretching my body out to rest seemed such a luxury. I was so thoroughly exhausted I quickly fell into a welcome sleep. I slept without waking, but as I slept, I dreamed, and when I awoke I was only half rested. My unremembered dreams shrouded my thoughts like a dark veil. As I quietly prepared myself for the day, I struggled to remember those dreams, but the details remained elusive.

Mary was also up before first light, and we were soon ready to meet the day. Matthias, too, was up and about, anxious to find Jesus, but he was not preparing himself quietly. He clattered and banged about, his noise obviously aimed at reminding his host family that he was still there and should be fed, even though we told him we would get something from a food vendor in the city after we had found Jesus. One of the servants, awakened by Matthias' racket, got up and began preparing some food, but the anticipation of seeing Jesus left no room for food in my stomach. Mary evidently felt as I did and declined the servant's offer to quickly prepare something to tide us over until we had a chance to buy food in the city.

Having readied ourselves, I whispered to Matthias, "We're leaving. Catch up after you've eaten. We're headed straight into the city." With that, we stepped out the front door into the cold, predawn air, and began to make our way through the darkness toward Jerusalem. I could hear Matthias sputtering when we left with no breakfast. Lazarus and Martha were up now to see us off, and there would be food soon, but Matthias was afraid he would lose his connection with me if he waited for it. Even after the conversation of last night, he still wanted to be associated with the new king's mother. He had missed Jesus' planning meeting the evening before, but still wanted to be in the inner circle. Matthias felt it necessary to show Jesus where he had been—that he had gone to fetch me.

As we made our way to the road that led from Bethany into the Holy City, Matthias caught up with us. The horse had been reclaimed by its owner the evening before, so he was now on foot, and a little out of breath. Since Mary and I were two women alone in the darkness, it was somewhat reassuring to have a man there, even if it was a man that I could only trust to let me down when the going got rough. At least now I was not under his control. I no longer had to depend on him to get me where I needed to be, but he was responsible for my getting this far at this time and I was grateful for that.

What security I found in Matthias' presence, however, quickly faded. A rapidly growing foreboding within me had begun with the gray mist of forgotten dreams. In the brilliant moonlight, Matthias caught a glimpse of my somber face and grew concerned. "You do think this is the day, don't you? Today would be perfect!" I heard in his voice a quiet laughter that stood in defiance of the impending danger of which we had been warned the evening before. I knew he wanted to discuss what lay ahead today, but I was struggling under such an oppressive feeling that I did not answer. Then Matthias grew quiet, too. I wanted to say something to him that would make a difference—put him more in touch with what Jesus was really doing, but if I did answer, what would I say? I knew that Matthias fought doubts, as did I, but I with more determination. For me, it was my son and my God that drew me—for him, a possible position of power, of prestige. He had seen with his own eyes that Jesus could overcome death. But, in truth, what could that mean in the face of Roman might? I wondered. And Matthias? He continued to struggle, and I did not know how to help. He was so close to Truth itself, but for the wrong reason. Would he ever see?

The growing sense that none of this was real—it was a bad dream; or I was an invisible observer of something that was happening to someone else; or I was a participant in another's nightmare—was heightened when I saw, near the road, in the eerie shadows of moonlight mixed with the first faint light of dawn, a wanted poster.[1] It named Jesus of Nazareth! My Jesus...I knew he was a wanted man! But seeing the poster added to the sense of unreality that had already pervaded my being. Surely none of this was happening. My Jesus was a good man!

I could not bear to think about the evident danger, so I tried to stop my mind from functioning and simply set one foot in front of the other, determined to fight anything from within or without that would keep me from finding my son. My mind, unable to keep quiet, fled from the pres-

---

1. There no doubt were posters out on Jesus, since the authorities had been seeking his arrest, and wanted posters were used in those days.

ent in order to protect me. Memories of Joseph burst into my mind. How I wished he were beside me now! Oh, how I longed for him. The last time I had come down this road in search of Jesus, Joseph with all his strength and faith was by my side. It seemed so long ago, and I had been so frightened then, but now... the danger seemed overwhelming... but, no! I would not allow myself to think of the danger! In self-defense, my mind clung to thoughts of the past. I remembered the twelve-year-old voice saying, "Didn't you know that I would be in my Father's house?" Those words brought me to the present with a new freshness! His Father's house! Was it a clue? Perhaps... Yes, I would go to the temple and look there for my son. With some direction in mind I walked faster, wondering if Jesus would be lost from me until the third day, as he had been when he was twelve. I shuddered and hoped not!

Mary kept pace, and Matthias followed behind. We were passing Gethsemane now, that olive grove with a press, where oil was forced from the fruit, and where Jesus and his friends liked to go to pray and be alone. It was the perfect place, he said. The hollow trees, some of them ancient, were short and stubby from having old limbs removed for wood and new limbs grafted on. The eerie, varying shapes, and the low-growing limbs, made it impossible to simply look through the grove to see what was there. Here, just a stone's throw from the city, the trees provided seclusion at any time, and a cool refuge in the heat of the day.

Perhaps Jesus was here now! But, no. not at this time of day. I would not spend time looking here. I was headed for the temple. Still, my eyes searched among the trees as I continued my determined walk. Unknown to me, only a short time before, my son had been here for the last time. Here he had prayed in great agony. And here, only a short distance from the path I now walked, he had been betrayed by Judas—the treasurer of his little group—and had been badly beaten in a typical Roman arrest, coming through it with a battered nose and blackened eyes. The soldiers always made sure that the marks of arrest remained on their victims for some time. Here Peter had tried to help, but Jesus would have no part of violence on his behalf.

I hurried along the very path where Jesus had been led as most of his followers left him. Crossing the Kidron, that ditch that carried the sewage away from Jerusalem, we started up the hill toward the walled city. The light of day was claiming its victory over darkness now. The wall that loomed above me glowed with the warmth of the newborn sun that caressed my back and comforted me. God was still in control![2]

We had encountered no one thus far—the road was deserted before the dawn, but as we passed through the gate into the shadowy city, I saw the figure of a man coming near. Once again I felt the cold edge of fear, but almost immediately, it was relieved by a familiar voice. "Mother of Jesus, is that you?" Coming closer, I saw John, the disciple whom Jesus loved so deeply. We hurried toward each other, and stretching out his arms, he gripped me tightly in a protecting embrace. "Oh, Mother, I heard that you were here. I was hoping it wasn't true—that you were still in Capernaum where you would be safe. I didn't want you to see what's happening. Mary... he's been arrested! The Romans beat him up pretty badly." He glanced at Martha's sister. "I'll take you both back home to Martha and Lazarus. You mustn't see this."

As I struggled with John's words, I briefly glimpsed Matthias slipping away to be swallowed up by the dark shadows of the city. He would not identify with someone under Roman arrest. John had caught hold of my arm and was gently and firmly turning me toward Bethany. Planting my foot firmly on the road, I stopped him. The need to assert myself snapped me out of that sense of unreality that had gripped me along the way. "You know I can't stay away. He is my son!" Tears were choking my voice. "I will be there for him in his suffering, no matter what it costs me." Suffering? What had I said?! Was God preparing me for something, as any mother who will see her child suffer must be prepared?

"Suffering?" I looked at John. His face was still. He did not answer me.

We stood looking at each other for a moment. Then he spoke again. "Mary, this could cost you your life! You cannot be identified with a man who has been arrested by the Romans."

"It doesn't matter," I said quietly, but firmly. The loneliness of being Jesus' mother during the years of his ministry came flooding back. There was no one who understood my position, no one I could tell my deepest thoughts to, except Jesus, and he had had other responsibilities. Life the last three years had been difficult, but I would not have changed places with anyone. Jesus was my son and all that mattered to me now was

2. The rising sun each morning was a reminder to God's people that God was still in control. (East is still at the top of maps in that part of the world, because it is the most important direction.)

that my son was hurting, and I must go—I would go—to him. My safety was not an issue.

"It matters to me," John said.

My eyes met his with the sternness of a Roman soldier. "Show me where he is, John," I said quietly; the tears had stopped.

As I stood facing John, awaiting his decision—to show me the way or let me try to find Jesus on my own—I heard clearly but dimly, through the still morning air, the beginning of the rituals at the temple. Preparations were beginning for the Passover feast that would be eaten this evening.[3] The words of the singing of the priests could barely be heard, but I knew them by heart: "I will extol you my God and King!" they sang. As those words drifted high into the heavens, other priests, who would later preside at the sacrifices of the lambs, were leading that very God whose praises were being sung—that very God, now incarnate in human flesh—to Pilate for trial. This was how they would extol their God!

As John consented to accompany me and we turned in the direction of the palaces of the High Priest and Pilate where Jesus was being tried, we heard the frightened bleating of the Passover lambs that had been cleansed and prepared for sacrifice and were now being led toward the temple area. Numbering about ten thousand they would be kept in Solomon's Stables beneath the temple until time for the sacrifices. All their skins were pure and without blemish and care would be taken to keep them that way until those same perfect skins were ripped off their backs at the sacrifice. As we hastened on our way, listening to the begging sounds of the lambs, Pilate was ordering that the Lamb of God be scourged—his perfect skin torn and ripped away from his back.

Pilate gave the order for the scourging, but he was not pleased about it. He had heard of Jesus' teachings and it seemed clear enough that if there had to be a "messiah" for these Judean people—and it seemed there had to be—Jesus would be the best one as far as Rome was concerned. If his teachings actually caught on among the Jews, it might make this difficult people easier to rule. Yes, it would be good if this Jesus of Nazareth could continue, at least for a time, but it was not that simple. Pilate needed to keep the priests calm during the festival, and they were the ones who had

---

3. Passover in the Gospel according to St. John, fell on Friday evening instead of Thursday evening as in the other Gospels. Therefore, as the lambs were being prepared for sacrifice, so was Jesus, the Lamb of God!

brought Jesus for judgement. Pilate suspected that they had brought Jesus to him not because Jesus would be a problem to Rome, but because he was a problem to the religious establishment of the Judeans.[4] In any case, Pilate could not risk a riot at this point, and any decision he made could bring one on. Perhaps Jesus could survive a scourging and the priests would be satisfied with something barely short of death.

Jesus was taken to the back room—the soldiers' quarters—out of sight. There his clothing was stripped from him, and his back was lashed repeatedly with a whip that was made just for such scourgings. It had a wooden handle which held strips of leather into which bits of metal or bone had been embedded. Little by little, Jesus' flesh was ripped away by the lashing, and, by the time the soldiers had finished, the flesh was thoroughly shredded and parts of the back bone and ribs were exposed. Then salt was thrown into the wounds, and when Jesus still lived (the salt often brought death), the soldiers proceeded to play "crown the king" with him, as was their habit with prisoners who were possibly headed for crucifixion. Lots were cast among these who were helplessly appointed to carry out the cruel imaginings of Roman rulers. The winners of this gambling would clothe the victim, before he was taken back to Pilate. The third place winner would get to throw the "royal cloak"—a scrap of purple cloth—over Jesus' torn and bleeding back. The second place winner would place a "royal scepter" in a hand so weak it could scarcely grasp the reed. The one with the highest number of points, of course,—first place—had the honor of pressing the crown of thorns upon the bloodied head. The soldiers had clothed Jesus, and they were completing their ritual by taunting and slapping him and spitting on him when we arrived outside the walled courtyard where the accusers and a small group of supporters—about fifteen people altogether—awaited the return of the soldiers and the scourged Savior.

---

4. When the Bible mentions Jews, it is usually making a geographical reference and would be better translated Judeans or Southerners.

CHAPTER 15

The Trial

At the gate into the courtyard, John spoke briefly to the gatekeeper. She was an acquaintance of his, since he had often come here to take orders for fish, and she let us slip through the gate and into the walled area that lay between Pilate's palace and the palace of the high priest, Caiaphas.[1] I had hardly had time to wonder at a woman being in such a position when I noticed that there were several priests present in the beautifully landscaped courtyard along with a few other people. They were all facing in the direction of the soldiers' quarters as though they were waiting for something. We worked our way across the back of the group and around to the side, stopping in the shadow of a bush. Now we were in a position to see some of what was going on without being noticed.

At first it seemed that nothing was happening, but then we saw Pilate come out. He knew that the soldiers had finished the work appointed them, and that Jesus was, as a result, about three-quarters dead. Pilate looked out at the crowd for a few moments, and then he announced, "I'm having the prophet, Jesus of Nazareth, brought back to you now. I find no wrong in him!" My heart leapt! Pilate found no wrong in him! Did this mean he would release him, unharmed? Was this how Jesus would establish his reign? Would he win Pilate over and work through Rome to establish the kingdom? My hope struggled to grow, but that gray cloud that had hovered over me since morning served as a damper.

I did not yet know that Jesus had been scourged. I had heard of people being executed by scourging, and I knew it was a horrible thing, but up until now I had no idea what it was really like. Presently, however, the soldiers brought Jesus out, properly punished and adorned, the reed still in

---

1. Rome appointed the high priests and kept an eye on them. Pilate's palace and the palace of the High Priest were separated only by a courtyard.

his hand, the crown of thorns on his head, his clothing restored to him for the moment. Pilate could see Jesus before I could, and I saw the procurator wince when Jesus appeared. I wondered if he had been beaten worse than most when he was arrested. At any rate, from Pilate's reaction, I thought that whatever had happened to Jesus, it must have been enough to satisfy the crowds. Reclaiming his composure, Pilate had Jesus turned toward the crowd and said,

"Behold the man."

"Yes! Behold the man!" I thought. "Behold humanity as it is intended to be!" Dreams of the wondrous years I had had with my son temporarily blinded me, but then clearly seeing his appearance, I corrected my thoughts. "Behold humanity! Behold what our nature does to others!"

Either way, whatever Pilate meant, I beheld him... there was my boy—face swollen almost beyond recognition, dried trickles of blood testifying to the piercing wounds of the thorns, his robe—sucked down, blackened, and held close to his back by the same blood that bathed his legs and feet. Something like a reed hung limply in his hand. He had been abused beyond belief.

My breath caught in my chest at the sight of him and saliva flooded my mouth as my stomach rebelled. "Ohhh, my son...," I groaned slightly. Nothing could have prepared me for this! I swallowed hard as a black circle engulfed the edges of my vision.

As the darkness grew and moved silently inward, mercifully removing me from a full consciousness of the growing tragedy, I heard, at what seemed a great distance, a familiar voice—Matthias, I thought—along with the voices of the priests and other leaders crying out, "Lift up! Lift up![2] Crucify him!" Then the encroaching blackness swallowed my consciousness, and I knew no more of that dreadful scene. John told me later that Pilate had taken Jesus inside for a time and then had brought him out again and tried once more to release him. But his accusers began shouting "Crucify him!" The shouts gradually shook me back into a state of consciousness.

John's arm was still gripping me tightly, keeping me on my feet, when I became aware of my surroundings and heard Pilate's cry, "Shall I

2. The people cried, "airo," Greek for "lift up," a term used for "crucify," because of the way the men were lifted to the cross, as explained later in this book. The irony is that the term could also refer to glorifying Jesus, although that is not what the crowd meant.

crucify your king?"

Then came the screams of the priests, "We have no king but Caesar!" There was a nervous sort of hilarity in the pitch of their voices as they realized they were about to have the blood they sought, and my heart broke in disbelief. These same voices would later complete the celebration of the Passover—a holy day of our God—by singing, "It is better to take refuge in the Lord than to put any trust in princes." Could they not see who Jesus was? Could they not see that it was the only begotten son of God whose life they sought? I felt so helpless. These priests, above all, should recognize their God!

In my desperation I was about to cry out, to try, myself, to put an end to this foolishness. Perhaps someone would listen to the prisoner's mother! But then I heard a distant bleating—the morning was passing quickly and the lambs were being led into place for the sacrifice which would begin at noon—and my half-conscious mind escaped to years long past. My Jesus was young again—a small boy. I saw him clearly, near the temple listening to the same bleating that I was hearing now. Tears were streaming down over his soft cheeks. With tenderness, I watched Joseph squat down in front of Jesus to talk with him. Jesus had just realized for the first time that all the innocent lambs that he was hearing and asking to see were to be killed. Joseph was trying to soothe him by explaining why it was so. Sitting down cross-legged on the ground, Joseph pulled Jesus into his lap. Jesus sat with his back against Joseph, Joseph's chin barely touching the top of the child's head. Putting his arms snug around the small boy, Joseph began to tell him the stories that lay behind the sacrifices and why they were performed here on the altar rock.

"My dear little one," Joseph had said, "it is not that we do not love the lambs and so wish them dead, but rather it is that we love God so much, and this is a way of showing our love."

"Why would God want you to kill a lamb?" sobbed Jesus.

"Well, Jesus, it is not so much that God wants us to kill a lamb. It is just that we must give him something important and something that helps us remember who we are. If we gave him something that meant nothing to us, it would mean nothing as a gift, so we bring something that we love, something that is hard for us to give up. In this desert land that God has given us, we have depended heavily upon sheep for life itself. Unlike other animals, they are able to adapt to this harsh land and thrive here, and they provide us with milk and meat, and wool for clothing and blankets, and skins for buckets and for wineskins, and so much else. We could not live in this land without them. So, when we give the best of our flock to God, it is a sacrifice for us and a way of saying that we know that we can give away the best of what we need, because in the end, it is God who provides. It is a way of reminding us that it is not ourselves that we must rely on, but rather our Creator and the Giver of Life.

"But there is more to it than that, my son, and I think that you are old enough to understand. You have been a good boy and have learned the stories of God well."

Jesus nodded seriously, very intent on Joseph's words. "Through your learning, you know that this place where we come today is the place where many of those stories happened.[3]

Jesus looked up at Joseph, his eyes filled with wonder.

"Inside the temple is a rock that the great altar is built upon," Joseph said. "Now, upon that rock, in ancient times, there grew a tree. It was the tree of the knowledge of good and evil. And, you know, that is the tree from which Eve picked the fruit and gave it to Adam, and they both sinned. So the first sin happened right there on the rock where God got the dust to form Adam in the first place. And beside this same rock, the first murder was committed when Cain killed Abel. And Abel's blood fell upon the rock and ran into the earth. Later after people grew so wicked that God decided to wash sin from the earth with a flood, old Noah's ark landed on this rock, and from here his family tried to make a new beginning. But sin continued and finally our Father Abraham, who tried to do whatever God wanted, came here to this same rock.[4] Here he first received the promise from God that he would have descendants and one of them would be a blessing to the whole world. Here he came to sacrifice his own son Isaac, because God asked him to. Do you remember what happened then?" Joseph looked at Jesus, whose little head nodded seriously. "Well then, tell me," Joseph prodded.

Jesus took a gulp of air. The tears no longer streamed, but his little chest still jerked in rhythm with the silenced sobs. He turned his head to the side and tilted it up to see Joseph's face. With his round black eyes fixed

---

3. The oral tradition places many of the stories at this particular spot.

4. Since the Holy Land is only about one hundred miles long and forty miles wide, history is piled upon history. The oral traditions and the teachings of the rabbis along with the Bible, place these many events in this one place. Jesus would have known these teachings.

on Joseph's, Jesus began, "God gave Isaac back to his father, and there was a ram caught in the brush that God gave Abraham for the sacrifice." Jesus bit his lip. "But, Father, that was not a lamb. It was full grown."

"But it was no less valuable," said Joseph, returning Jesus' gaze with all the seriousness he would give to any adult asking questions. "The point is, the ram was very valuable to Abraham, the shepherd, because it would be the father of many lambs, but it was not so valuable to him as was Isaac, his son. The ram's life was given in place of Isaac's life."

"So when you give a lamb, it takes my place?" asked Jesus, the tears now merely streaks on his dusty cheeks, the sucking of the sobs nearly stopped.

"Yes," said Joseph, "but there is more to the story." He smiled down at Jesus, squeezing his arms tightly around him. "You know the story of the Passover, how, when we were slaves in Egypt, the angel of death passed over all the houses that had lamb's blood on the door?"

Jesus nodded his head, at the same time rubbing his nose vigorously with the back of his hand and taking a long, deep breath.

"God commanded that every year we should sacrifice a lamb and eat it as our ancestors did, so that we will remember the mighty things God did to set us free."

"I know," said Jesus, turning sideways on Joseph's lap and snuggling up close.

"So each year we bring our lambs, because God said we should, and when we give them to God we remember that one time, long ago, the lives of lambs were given to save us, and so we hold our lamb up to God and say, 'This is me, God, that you saved by a lamb. I give myself to you because I love you so much.' Then when the lamb is killed, we take its blood, its life, in a bowl to the altar and say, 'This is my life, God. I give it to you, because I love you so much!'"[5]

Joseph stopped to see how Jesus was doing. He was such a little boy to be hearing so much, but he was hearing. "But why do we come here, Father? Why don't we just sacrifice a lamb at home?"

"We come here because this is God's holy mountain where David brought the ark of the covenant and Solomon built the first temple. We come here because so much of our history is here and this place helps us

---

5. The Passover sacrifice was not for forgiveness, as some sacrifices were, but rather a giving of self.

remember who we are. We come here because it is a special, different thing we do that helps identify us as God's special people."

Again Joseph paused and Jesus spoke in his small child's voice. "May I go with you when you take the lamb to give our lives to God?" He tilted his small face toward Joseph with a look that said he hoped the answer would be yes, and at the same time, he hoped even more that the answer would be no.

"No, not until you are thirteen, Jesus," Joseph replied gently. "Until then, you must stay with your mother. But when you are old enough to come with me, you will be amazed at what you see." Jesus focused on Joseph with his whole being, and Joseph's eyes drifted to wonders to be seen again. "The altar is made of limestone, and it is twenty two feet high, so high that there have to be steps so that the priests can climb up to make the offerings. It's about as high as that house over there. It is such an awesome sight, that many are speechless and in tears when they see it, and some men tremble because it is a place where we draw so near to God." I saw Joseph stop there and I remembered how he had described the scene to me. How the blood of the sacrifices was thrown against the altar and then water was thrown to keep the blood from congealing. Before the day of sacrifice was completed, the priests would be wading in blood up to their ankles. But Jesus did not need to hear this, and Joseph spared him.

Jesus had laid his head against Joseph's chest then. "Will it always be so, Abba? (He always switched to "Daddy" when he felt very close to Joseph.) Will our people always come here to sacrifice lambs? I think I would like it to not always be so. Maybe someday we could just give ourselves to God and not have to kill a lamb."

"No, my little one. It will not always be so. Someday, God promises, our people will be a blessing to all the peoples of the world. Then it will be like it was in the garden before we sinned. Then we will be very close to God and there will be no more killing. Not even a lion will kill a lamb, but they will lie down together and be friends."

Jesus thought about this as a young boy will, and then he looked up at Joseph and said, "But Abba, how are we to be a blessing to all people?"

Joseph smiled and his eyes revealed hope in the midst of this troubled land. "Through us will come a descendent of Abraham, an anointed one, whom God will use to free all people from all oppression for all time. You see, my son," Joseph looked at Jesus as though he were conveying the greatest message of all time to one worthy to receive it, "this one will return us to the relationship that we had with God here in the garden in the beginning, and in God's presence our troubles will cease. There will be no more sin or death or sorrow…" Jesus watched Joseph and listened with wonder. He always loved it when Joseph sat down to talk with him, and especially if it had to do with the things of God.

As Joseph went on with the stories, his voice became a droning and my mind began to gently shift me back to the present. I remembered thinking that this little one—my son—was to be that blessing. The Blessing had come! And my mind returned me fully to the present—to look at the Blessing now! He who was to free us, was now experiencing oppression at its worst and facing possible death at the hands of Rome. This one who had raised Lazarus from death… would he now die? And if he did, would any of those who came to offer their lambs and their lives to God know that the Messiah whom God had sent was suffering at the same time as their lambs?

Oh, this people! God loved them so much, for though their devotion to their God was often misdirected, still they were dedicated to that one who had formed them. But now was the time for the Blessing to come, and few of them recognized it, and probably none of them, including me, realized that a final lamb was about to be sacrificed, namely God's Lamb, my son.

Perhaps it was the sound of the lambs and the memory of happy holidays long past that finally brought me fully aware again, but what I saw when my eyes were opened made me wish I was not conscious. There was my son, shouldering the crosspiece of a cross and struggling to begin his walk toward death. I cringed at the sight of that heavy piece of olive wood bearing down upon his drooping shoulder and bowed back, grinding the cloth of his robe down into his bleeding body. Jesus staggered and stumbled forward as he felt the full impact of his load. Then, catching his balance, he took one painful trembling step. This was followed by another, and then another, as he, my son and the Son of God, carried the wood toward the place of the sacrifice, just as Isaac had done. I wanted to run to him, but I knew there was nothing I could do. The Romans would seize me and throw me back—of that there was no doubt—and seeing me attacked for coming to his aid would only add to Jesus' pain. I felt so helpless, and I knew pain as I had never known it before. "Ohhh, Simeon," I groaned deep within myself, "I had no idea it would be like this!"

My mind rebelled against the testimony of my eyes and ears! My son—God's son!—had been sentenced to death. But it couldn't be!! The trial was illegal! I knew it, and the priests knew it! Among our people, capital offenses could be tried neither at night nor on the eve of a festival day, and this had been a violation of both. And when there was a trial, and a person was found guilty and sentenced to die, there had to be a lapse of time between sentencing and execution. They couldn't be executing him now! They must wait! And there were no positive witnesses. They could not sentence someone to death without positive witnesses! All the laws were being broken. If only there were some way to get the executioners to wait until I could find someone to uphold the law… but even if I could stop them, who would I get to set things straight? The leaders of our people had asked for the death sentence. Rome had agreed and was about to carry it out. To whom could I turn for help? There was no earthly authority left. I knew there was nothing I could do. But at least I could be there.

John and I together followed the procession of Jesus and his crucifiers out of the courtyard and into the street. By now, people were out and about taking care of last minute details for the Passover celebration. With eighty thousand additional people in town, the narrow streets were nearly impassable, so we struggled to stay close to Jesus. It was hard to see him, and I kept pressing ahead in the crowd to try to stay near my boy. Once, when the narrow way widened temporarily, I actually pressed ahead of him without realizing it, and then suddenly I looked over my shoulder and there he was. At first I thought it was someone else—he was so crushed and bruised—and I was puzzled that someone else was undergoing the same thing so near. Then I realized it was my Jesus, and my heart ached at not recognizing him. I saw him fall under the terrible weight of his cross, and a soldier raised his whip, threatening to lash him, to drive him on, but one of the officers grabbed the soldier's wrist. "We can't crucify him if he's already dead," he growled. Jesus appeared to me to be dead, and I prayed for his sake that he was! Ohhh, my son!

The darkness began to close in on my field of vision again, and John, seeing what was happening, gripped me firmly, one arm across my back, his other hand on my arm, holding me up as my knees began to give way. "Mary!" he hissed in my ear. "Not now! Rome mustn't see!" Suddenly it was Jesus gripping me firmly at the wedding at Cana, and it was Jesus' voice saying, "Not now!" My dear Jesus! I had to get a grip on myself. I had to trust. I had to be here for him. The crowd was moving past us now. I glimpsed Jesus struggling on. Then the crowds closed in, and I lost sight of him again.

We followed closely, the procession was moving very slowly. Jesus was setting the pace, he who was carrying a pressing load—and dying. Occasionally, the movement would stop all together and the crowd would groan. I guessed numbly that Jesus had fallen again or just had trouble moving forward—I could not bear to speculate. Somewhere along the way, I did not see where, Rome took the load from Jesus' back and forced it upon the shoulder of another—one Simon of Cyrene. Still, the two hundred yards to Golgotha went slowly. In some ways I hoped we would never get there; I hoped that I would wake up and see Jesus' face smiling at me; I hoped it would take so long to get there that God would intercede… but on another level, I just wished we were there and that the suffering was over.

We moved through the city gate, down the hill, around the Pool, and from there I saw that piece of limestone in the midst of the old quarry rising twenty-two feet into the air, the same as the altar. Soft limestone, it was—no good for buildings—so the workers had quarried around it, leaving it in favor of good hard stone. Now it stood alone in the shape of a skull, providing a perfect place for Rome to crucify, here in plain view of all who would enter the Holy City. Above me I saw the upright pieces of the crosses, all standing in their places, ghoulishly stark, as though one crucifixion more or less didn't really matter. "Trust me." I could hear Jesus' words whispering in my soul, but Simeon's words followed, "and a sword will pierce your soul, too." That old prophet had told me so long ago that this would happen. Surely I could trust my son. If this was how things had to be; I would try.

CHAPTER 16

Death Comes

It was noon when we reached the top of the hill, and I realized that a strange darkness had settled over the land. When I first noticed it, I thought, with some frustration, that I must be losing consciousness again, but then I realized that others noticed the darkness as well. The people around me seemed frightened and uncertain. Even the soldiers grew edgy, and one of them drew near to Simon and sharply kicked the beam that he carried. That kick sent the beam crashing to the ground, knocking Simon off his feet, but landing clear of him. Simon quickly righted himself, and scurrying away, disappeared into the crowd. As I watched Jesus, who was nearby and barely able to stand, the trumpet sounded at the temple ordering the sacrifice of the lambs to begin.[1] At the same instant the order was given to begin the crucifixion of Jesus.

The soldiers required no urging. Acting immediately upon the order, a Centurion grabbed Jesus' arm and jerked him sideways. Proceeding in the usual manner of a crucifixion, the soldier began to remove Jesus' clothing. The partially dried blood had bound cloth and flesh together as one, and now they were torn apart as the Centurion ripped the cloth from Jesus' back. The blood came forth anew, and I saw for the first time what had been done to my boy. There he was before me, beaten—his shredded back bleeding—his body as naked as the day he was born—except for the crown of thorns which he continued to wear on his head.

Thus was Jesus crucified. I watched, ashamed for his nakedness, as was Rome's intent, but not ashamed. For although this was the greatest horror I could ever imagine—seeing my son suffering and humiliated—it was weighing down on me with a numbing pain—still, I was proud of him, as I had always been.

Once Jesus had been relieved of his clothing, he was placed, spread-

---

1. Sacrifice of the Passover lambs began at noon.

eagle on the ground with the cross beam beneath his shoulders. Now I saw firsthand what I had only heard described before. The details had all been revealed in the talk among the women at the well in Nazareth, but I had not realized until now the full extent of the horror. You see, the husband of one of my neighbors, Aaron by name,[2] had been forced to help with a crucifixion when his family had made a trip to visit relatives. One of the young nephews in the family had been involved in some activity which Rome believed to be subversive, so he was crucified as an example to others. Poor Aaron had been forced to help carry the cross and then to watch all that was done to his beloved nephew. One heartless soldier had explained with great relish why the crucifixion was done as it was. There were details performed with precision that you and I would never even consider, and seeing it all, Aaron had never really recovered from the horror of that day. In his sad state, he would grab his wife, Sereth, and tell her over and over again what he had seen. And after she had listened and done her best to comfort him, she would come to the well seeking the comfort of other women. There she would tell us all that her husband had said. She would describe how the arms of the rebel were stretched out straight by two soldiers while the executioner drove spikes through his wrists[3] between the arm bones and just above the joint, taking care not to break the bones which were needed to support his weight and prolong his agony.

Now I saw step by step what I had heard Sereth describe, only this was not just some vivid description of something that happened to a stranger—or was it? How could this be true? Oh, my dear son! I was engulfed in a sense of unreality as I noted the care with which the centurion placed the spikes. Oh, Aaron, if only I had been more sympathetic! I watched while a system of ropes and pulleys was being fastened to that heavy piece of wood that Jesus had carried and to which he had now been nailed. Then the crosspiece, along with Jesus, was "lifted up" just as the crowd had demanded. Because of what I had heard from Sereth, I was not surprised when the two soldiers who had held Jesus down now carefully supported his weight while the cross beam was raised, positioned, and then dropped onto the vertical piece.

I wished Sereth had not told me so much. It would have been a comfort to imagine that Jesus' weight was being supported out of some

2. Again, fictitious characters are introduced for the sake of narrative and to provide facts concerning crucifixions.
3. The wrists were considered a part of the hands.

sense of mercy, rather than simply to ensure prolonged agony by guarding against broken bones. At the same time, care was being taken at the temple to ensure that none of the bones of the sacrificial lambs were broken, rendering the sacrifice invalid!

The two soldiers continued to support Jesus while a "throne" was positioned for him and nailed firmly to the cross. It was the same annoyingly thin piece of splintered acacia wood which Sereth had described. The crucified could rest his weight upon it, but it would tear his bare body with every move he made. With this in place, Jesus' feet were pushed up so that the knees were lifted and bent and the feet were fastened with a fig wood strap, and a single spike was driven through his heel bones and into the cross.[4] Now Jesus' weight was lowered onto his "throne," where he sat sideways, his body twisted and bent. The soldiers' work was done. They had now only to guard their prisoner as they awaited his death. And I, too, had only to wait. And as I waited, I thought of Aaron and Sereth and the young man whose suffering had caused so much grief for those he loved. And I thought of the thousands and thousands of men who had died on crosses, and of those who loved them and daily died a thousand deaths as they remembered. And I looked at Jesus and I ached. But even as I ached, I felt God's hand upon me, and I knew that strange unexplainable peace that I had first felt as I had trudged home from Elizabeth's, a pregnant teenager on her way to tell her betrothed that she carried a child that was not his.

As I stood there near the cross, I saw someone come and nail a sign to the cross beneath Jesus' feet.[5] It read, "Jesus of Nazareth, the King of the Judeans," and it was written in Hebrew, Latin, and Greek, so that all could read it. Golgotha, like an amphitheater of death, was the perfect place to show all who came into Jerusalem that here, too, Rome was in control! The Jews could put up signs[6] and they could make their demands, but here was a reminder that there would be Judean signs posted and demands made, only so long as Rome allowed it.

Of course, the sign that had been put on the cross was infuriating to those who had sought Jesus' death. Now that they had seen him to the cross, they wanted the credit. This sign made it look as though only Rome

4. Crucifixion was much different than we have imagined it. The body was kept low, the knees bent, the body twisted.

5. The cross being shaped like a "T," signs were placed beneath the crucified, although Matthew indicates that the sign was placed above his head.

6. Signs written in Hebrew, Greek, and Latin were posted on the wall around the sanctuary, warning all non-Jews to keep out.

wanted to be rid of Jesus, and not the religious officials, who were fighting the spread of his teachings. So, some of them went running directly to Pilate to have the sign removed or, at least, changed.[7] They wanted it made clear that they did not see Jesus as their king.

Jesus was very close to me as I stood there, since the cross was not more than six feet tall, even with the crosspiece on top. Rome deliberately kept the crosses short. They did not want people looking up to the crucified and venerating them. They wanted the victims of this cruel punishment kept low, where people could look down into their eyes, spit on them, jeer at them, and slap them, as some did in hopes of winning Rome's favor.

As I stood so near, offering my presence to my son and my Lord, I realized that there were others standing near me. There was John, of course, but when I looked around, my sister was there! And Mary, wife of Clopas! And Mary Magdalene! Mary of Bethany, who had come into town with us on that morning, had gotten separated from us somewhere between the site of the trial and Golgotha. Rather than fight the escalating crowding in the streets, she had gone quickly to tell others what was happening. These friends had come. I looked at them gratefully, and they looked back at me. Their eyes were filled with sorrow and pain. It was good to see them. When grief fills the soul, another human being can lighten the load. I had no idea how true that is until I saw these kindred souls standing here, defying the danger, lending support. We said nothing, only drank in one another's presence for a few moments. Tears rolled down my cheeks and theirs, too. Then our gaze returned to Jesus, and we just stood there together in that open area in the presence of our dying Lamb.

Other lambs were dying at the same time in the temple, but in the temple, no women or children were allowed; no Gentiles or beggars or sick or disabled could be present at the slaughter; only clean, healthy, whole, adult, Jewish males. Here at this sacrifice, in the midst of the darkness that had fallen over the land, not unlike the darkness of the Holy of Holies, the inner sanctum of the temple, we could all be present. No one was excluded on the basis of race or sex or age or status—not the Gentiles who passed by, or perhaps stopped, because Jesus had been kind to them— not us women, who, aside from John, were the only followers of Jesus who had not deserted their dying friend—not the beggars, who were

7. John 19:21

unclean because of the food they scavenged—not those who had hoped to be healed, and now saw that hope being put to death—not the children, whose parents had brought them to see the crucifixion in hopes of deterring them from future crimes against Rome. Here at the cross, any and all could draw near to God, and no one would try to keep them away.

Two other men were lifted up on either side of Jesus, but I was only vaguely aware of them. Oh, I knew they were there, but the weight of my own son's suffering was so great I could bear no more. It pressed in upon me and grew heavier and heavier, and I wondered how much longer I could stand. Physically, the weight was tremendous, but it pressed in on my emotions as well, condensing and molding them into one large lump of growing pain that lay solidly beneath my breast bone, occasionally reaching out little fingers here and there to snatch back ounces of energy which it fed upon. I tended it with dry eyes now, and simply waited.

Jesus stirred, and my eyes fixed on him again. His head came up slowly, and a swollen tongue licked his hardening, misshapen lips. He gazed at those before him, who had put him on the cross, and then raising his puffed eyes toward the heavens as well as he could, he breathed, "Father, forgive them… they don't know… what they are doing." And he lowered his head slowly and his eyes closed again. I sat stunned. He had taught that we were to forgive… and we were to pray for our enemies, but… this prayer of his! In this prayer he released all control over his enemies. He not only forgave them and prayed for them, but he prayed for God to forgive them. If God forgave them, what would be their punishment for what they had done? Oh, my Jesus! Must I forgive those who hurt me, too? Could you not even die without teaching me to live?

I looked at my son, and I looked at those who leered at him. I struggled to forgive these who held no love for Jesus, and I could not. But because I knew it was Jesus' will, I sought God's help. And a strange thing happened. As I began to let go of the hatred I held for these men and my desire for them to finally know God's punishment for their sins, I felt an unfamiliar freedom filling me! In the midst of my agony at the suffering of my son, I felt a wondrous freedom… and a peace… and a strength… the pain could no longer drain me. God in his mercy, at my obedience, had given strength back to me. The enemy could not win! My heart swelled, my eyes drifted off, words spoken by the prophet Isaiah played in my mind, "Then your light shall break forth like the dawn, and your healing shall spring up quickly; your vindicator shall go before you, the glory of the Lord shall be your rear guard. Then you shall call, and the Lord will answer; you shall cry for help, and he will say, 'Here I am!'"[8]

But I soon forgot my new found freedom as my mind was captured by a commotion near the cross. With difficulty, my eyes came back into focus, and I saw to my horror that some of the soldiers were gambling for Jesus' clothing! I took a step in their direction, thinking I would tell them that I was his mother, and that I wanted his clothes, and they would give them to me. But John caught my shoulder with his hand, stopping me short. I looked at him questioningly with annoyance. My sudden desire for Jesus' clothing had blocked all judgement, as our desire for material things often does. All I could think was that I wanted to claim Jesus' robe! It was stiff with his hardened blood, but I longed to take it home. Feeling heavy again, I longed to be home. I was so tired, I longed for this whole horrible business to stop. Drifting into another world, I thought I would take Jesus' clothing and soak it and scrub the blood out of it, just as I had when he was small and had fallen and skinned his knee. I would get it clean, and I would keep it, and when I was lonely, I would take it out and hold it close to me… but the clothing was not to be mine. I knew it, and John's stern look and firm grip reminded me. The soldiers dreaded crucifixions, and one of the few perks was the victim's clothing, which they divided among themselves. Jesus' clothing was their clothing now.

I watched Jesus and the sound of the guards drifted far off to somewhere my ears no longer heard. Then the chief priests, who had gone to Pilate to demand that the sign be removed from the cross or changed to read, "This man said he was the King of the Judeans," returned. They were obviously perturbed—apparently they had not gotten what they wanted—and then they heard some of the passers-by jeering at Jesus.

"You who would destroy the temple and build it in three days, save yourself!"

"If you are the Son of God, come down from the cross."

That was all the priests needed to hear to get them started. They, along with the scribes and elders, began mocking Jesus.

"He saved others; he cannot save himself."

"He is the king of Israel; let him come down from the cross now, and we will believe in him."

8. Isaiah 58:8-9

"He trusts in God; let God deliver him now, if he wants to; for he said, 'I am God's Son.'"

I hoped he would come down! I hoped Jesus would show them once and for all who he was! After all, he *was* God's son. I knew that as no one else did. But I remembered him saying, "Do not resist evil," and surely this was evil at its finest, and he would not resist. But as I sat listening to the jeering, I realized that evil was not so much in the men who had crucified Jesus, because they did not choose this assignment. They were simply carrying out orders. But rather, evil was in these who called themselves men of God, who had looked into Jesus' face and did not recognize Goodness personified. But even in his dying form, Jesus was strong, and although I wished he would just show them who he was, he would not be taunted into doing something that he would not have done otherwise. Even now, they could not control him. If things were to have been different, he would have changed them before now. I knew that! But even knowing it—I would still have yelled back at the taunters. I would have yelled back, that is, if the weight of the pain in my chest had not grown so heavy. I was not sure I even had a voice. So they jeered... and I listened... and watched... and as I settled down and began to ask God's help again, some semblance of strength returned. I could feel the energy leaving the lump of pain in my chest and coming back into my system again. And feeling stronger, I continued to wait.

Then one of those who had been crucified with Jesus joined the jeering; "Are you not the Messiah? Save yourself and us!"

The other, in his weakened state, shot back "Where is your fear of God? You hang here dying with the same death sentence as him. But we earned it. This man shouldn't be here." He paused, and then addressed my son, "Jesus, remember me when you come into your kingdom."

As I struggled, this man, hanging there dying, expressed faith.

While all this was going on, Jesus did not move or respond in any way. The other two had not been scourged, and so were stronger. But now, Jesus raised his head weakly and turned it toward the revolutionary who supported him. With an authority that broke through his tenuous voice he spoke, each word an effort, "I tell you... today... you will be with me... in Paradise."

Then his head dropped down, and he was quiet again. He stayed that way for quite some time, and for a while, I thought that he was no longer conscious. Or perhaps he had died... and I hadn't noticed when it happened! I studied him carefully now. He rested on his "throne," his "crowned" head hung low against his chest. As I gazed at him, my throat swollen with grief, my eyes burning for lack of any more tears to shed, I allowed myself to wonder if this were even my Jesus at all. His appearance was so changed, it brought to mind Isaiah's description of the suffering servant,[9] which we had never considered messianic scripture, but which described Jesus now. His face was beyond recognition with swelling and discoloration. His skin, which I had cared for so gently and protected so carefully when he was a little child, was torn and scraped. Hardly a place on him was whole. The beating in the garden, the scourging at the hands of the soldiers, and his falling along the way had marred him horribly. His hair, that I had lovingly washed and combed so many times, was matted and stuck to him with sweat and blood. In fact, there was blood everywhere on him, and salt crystals glistened on his back and shoulders.

Just when I had nearly convinced myself that this was not my son, his body slipped from his throne, and he was jerked out of whatever state of shock had captured him. As his weight came down on the spikes that held his arms, his head came up. I could see his breathing stop as his chest was paralyzed by his weight hanging from his arms. He had hung there only a moment when his dazed eyes fell on me, and I saw the dim light of life come into them. Struggling to shift his weight to his feet, so that he could breathe again, Jesus managed to push back up onto his throne. His gaze fell on John then, and some look of relief came into his badly swollen eyes. Moving those eyes back to me and opening his mouth, he breathed through thick and swollen lips, rasping in a voice that was hardly his own, "Womannnn..."

Woman?! I was jolted from my grief. Did he call me woman?! It was an insult! My heart was torn! Was I no longer his mother, that he now called me woman? Ohhh...but then the wedding at Cana flashed into my mind. Perhaps he meant something else now, just as he did then.[10]

"Be...hold... your... son." The words were expelled, quietly, yet forcibly, from his mouth, and his chin dropped to his chest.

Yes, I beheld my son—what was left of him! Tears ran down my

9. Isaiah 52:13—53:12
10. Woman reminds us of Eve. Through Eve sin came into the world. Now through this woman's son, things are set straight. (See Chapter 9, The Wedding at Cana)

cheeks once again, as the pain in my chest nearly smothered me. I thought, now at last, with his head fallen, my son was dead. But then Jesus turned his face, and slowly raised his chin, until his eyes pointed toward the disciple standing beside me. For a moment I thought he would not speak, but then his eyes focused and his lips moved, "Bee...hold... yourrr... mmmotherrr," he breathed, and his head dropped again. John's arm slipped around my waist, and in spite of my pain, I had the peace and comfort of knowing that he would always care for me. I knew he would be the son Jesus himself had wanted to be and could not, because he was called for other things. In his agony, Jesus had provided for John and me by commending us to each other, but he had done even more than that. He had reminded me that God always provides, and, more often than not, it is through other people. It is strange how things like that run through one's mind at such times, but perhaps that is God's way of comforting us, too. God always somehow keeps our burdens from destroying us—keeps them from being more than we can bear.

As I stood there with these thoughts playing around in my mind, I felt something hit my robe. Looking down, I saw a drop of water soaking into the cloth, and then another hit, and I realized that it was not water, bur rather tears. John was crying. In fact, as I looked at him, I saw that his spent, dirty face was streaked with tears. I had not noticed before how much he was hurting. I was too engrossed in my own pain and the horror of what was taking place. I marveled now at how deeply John loved my son. How painful it was for him to stand here with me, but he would not leave as the others had. He would endure pain in order to support those he loved.

Once again, I thought that Jesus had died. He had slipped from the throne and had hung motionless for several seconds, suspended by the nails through his wrists and heels. Then flexing his arms and straining to straighten his legs what little was possible, he lunged his weight upward and, in the same motion, cried out, "My God! My Gooooddddddd!" It was as though a last burst of energy filled him and exploded into a cry of desperation. As his buttocks came to rest on his "throne" again, his chest and head fell forward, expelling the words, "Why have you forsaken me?"[11] I was still reeling with the impact of this cry of grief, when he spoke from

---

11. Jesus may be quoting Psalm 22. Bonhoffer points out that the Psalms are prayers that God has given us to pray in God's own words. The Psalms are noted for allowing us to express our deepest feelings exactly as they are.

his throne, "I thirssstt."

There was a jar standing there containing wine vinegar and gall that was to be given to the crucified as a pain killer, but instead of just giving it to him, some of the men began mocking him. They laughed and speculated that he was calling Elijah, and they jeered, "No, don't give it to him yet. Wait and see if Elijah will come!"

Cruel cackles of laughter crashed in on my ears, and Simeon's sword twisted. "Trust me! You won't understand, but trust me!" Jesus' voice rang in my mind. But then someone among them—I vaguely remember thinking it was Matthias, and that maybe he had not completely given up on Jesus—picked a weed that grows about thirty inches tall in that area—a branch of hyssop[12]—and he put a sponge on the end of the weed and dipped it into the vinegar and then held it up to Jesus' mouth. By this time, Jesus was hanging low again, breathing suspended, and the vinegar ran from the sponge as it was pressed against his mouth. Lunging upward one last time, in order to get air into his lungs, and inclining his head as if in prayer, Jesus screamed, "It is brought to completion!" "It is brought to peace"—"It has become as God intends," he was saying.[13] And he gave over his spirit—to the people to whom he had inclined his face—and to God to whom he whispered his final words, "Father, into your hands I commend my spirit." And Jesus went limp... and I knew that he was dead... and I slumped down onto the ground, my head hung in final disbelief and grief. This, then, is what very religious people, who are devoid of love, do to others. No wonder Jesus had gone to such extremes to teach the importance of loving at all times.

It was three o'clock. The sacrifice of the lambs was over. The sacrifice of The Lamb was over, and light returned to the land—and the curtain that separated the Holy of Holies from the world split in two, and, as the light entered the world, it entered the Holy of Holies as well. In its darkness, the world had become the inner sanctum that would contain the presence of God, and as Jesus died, that presence was opened to the whole world... And the earth shook.

---

12. The same weed that was used to smear the blood of the first Passover lambs on the doorposts of the houses of God's people in Egypt.

13. Jesus used the Greek word *tetelestai* a form of *teleios* which has the same meaning as the Hebrew word *shalom*. What Jesus did on the cross was "finished" in the sense that God's plan had been brought to completion—it was "whole." Things had become as God intended them to be, which is the meaning behind the Hebrew *shalom*, which we usually translate "peace."

CHAPTER 17

The Burial

The Sabbath and, this year, the Passover as well, would begin at sunset, and lest this doubly holy day be desecrated, the bodies would need to be off the crosses soon. Wielding the same hammer that had been used to nail Jesus to the cross, the Romans set out to shatter the legs of the men who had been crucified. Breaking their legs would hasten their deaths, but if it was still not enough, the men would simply be taken down, thrown into a cell somewhere, and left until the inevitable happened. When the executioners came to Jesus, they saw that he was already dead, and there was, therefore, no reason to break his legs. To ensure that he was indeed dead, one of the soldiers ran a sword into Jesus' side. Blood and water came running out of the wound, washing over his body, cleansing a small path as it rushed downward, fell to the ground, and sank into the earth. He was indeed dead.

I had been standing, and now I lowered myself to the ground, and sat with my head hanging nearly into my lap. The weight of the day's events pressed in on my chest, making breathing difficult. Passover was not supposed to be like this. It had been such fun in the past, a family time... Joseph, Jesus, and I together. My mind again rescued me from the crushing load of the present, taking me to more pleasant times... Passovers past. Jesus was twelve once again, and I could see him waiting in the women's court of the temple with Elizabeth, John, and me. Joseph and Zachariah would be coming out of the men's court soon, bringing the Passover lamb that had been sacrificed for our families. Joseph had told Jesus that this year he and John were old enough to carry the lamb from the temple to the house within the city walls where we would feast. So, the boys had positioned the four of us near the entrance into the men's court. They wanted to be as close as possible when the men appeared.

As we waited, John and Jesus were in constant motion in spite of the crowd. I watched them with pleasure, our boys, so close to manhood. They kept reading the signs that were chiseled out of limestone slabs and set at intervals around the men's court for all to see. The signs warned all foreigners, in three different languages, to stay out or risk death! None but the adult males of God's people could witness the sacred rites that went on inside. Reading the signs only added to the excitement. They were feeling brave and grown up and safe, even from Rome, in this house of God. Then the boys saw the men coming, Joseph holding the sacrificed lamb in his arms. Fairly bouncing with the joy of the day, those two ran to Joseph, anxious to receive the lamb. Elizabeth and I watched as Jesus carefully took the sizeable ball of wool into his arms. The carcass had been wrapped securely in its own hide, the legs tucked carefully inside the body cavity to prevent their being broken and disqualifying the animal as our Passover lamb. Jesus and John took turns carrying it tenderly as we hurried toward the room Zachariah had secured for us.[1] We lost sight of the boys in the crowd, and Elizabeth and I smiled at one another with pride. Our sons were old enough now to go off on their own. They could hurry with all the intensity of youth, and we could move at our own pace, knowing they would be at our destination when we arrived.

We enjoyed our walk together that year, marveling at the goodness of the day. We had once again given our lives to God through the lamb, and that alone made this day like no other. Our hearts and spirits soared. Now we would cook and feast together, recalling the mighty acts of God in the Exodus, remembering how God had saved our people through the blood of a lamb. Then we would eat together our own lamb, just as our ancestors had done so many years ago, and as our people had continued to do every year since. It was a wonderful holiday. I was warmed by the memories of that last feast with our sons as boys—but then, that was the year we had lost Jesus on our return home. He had been as one who was dead, until he was restored to us on the third day. My mind pulled me forward in time. Jesus had told some of his followers that he would die and on the third day He would rise from the dead.

"Trust me," I heard his voice trailing down through time, and I looked at Jesus' body hanging there.

"Could it be," I wondered, " … on the third day?" That would be after the Sabbath was ended. He had raised Lazarus. Could he raise him-

---

1. The Passover meal was always eaten within the city walls.

self? Did I dare to hope?

"Trust me!" The words sounded clearly in my mind.

I lifted my head, and through eyes that stared for no reason, I watched, emotionless, spent, as the soldiers removed the two revolutionaries from their crosses. One screamed in pain, wringing from my body yet another twinge of sorrow, and the other slipped into unconsciousness, as they were dragged away to cells where they would be left to die.

My eyes returned to Jesus, and for the first time, I saw a richly dressed man standing near the cross. The crowd had dispersed while I was in a time past. There were only a handful of soldiers, this man, and a couple of men who appeared to be his servants. He seemed to be giving them instructions, and when he had finished, one of them took hold of Jesus' body and gently lifted up while the other began working the spikes out of the wood of the cross. Now John was there, speaking to the wealthy man. Then, charging his men to work with care lest the bones, which had already been damaged by the sawing of the spikes, be broken; the rich man and the disciple walked toward me. Stopping and kneeling down in front of me, the man spoke.

"Mother of Jesus," he began, looking into my eyes, his own filled with a deep and gentle concern. "I am Joseph from the town of Arimathea. I have long been an admirer of your son and his work. When I realized what had happened to him here today, I drew upon my business dealings with the Prefect to get an audience with him. Pilate has given me permission to take Jesus' body and place it in my own tomb." He paused here for a moment, searching my wearied face with his eyes, and then went on. "I recently purchased this garden, here, next to Golgotha, to use for my family tomb. The first burial chamber has been carved out of the rock wall that was once the side of this old quarry. It's just over there about twenty-five yards. If you look, perhaps you can see it." He motioned with his arm, but I did not look. I felt as though I had no strength left in my body, and it seemed a monumental task to lift my head and turn it in the direction he pointed. When I did not look, Joseph seemed a little anxious. "I have Pilate's permission to take the body, and I would like to get some ointment and spices on it and get it wrapped and into the burial chamber before the Sabbath begins. I've not much time if it is to be done at all properly. I'm sorry to push you, Mother. I'm asking for your blessing in going ahead with taking Jesus away. Is it all right?"

I lifted my face toward him. "Let me hold him," I said with resolve. I had come for a coronation of a different type. They had taken away his clothing. I would have one thing, and that was to hold my son one last time.

"What?" Joseph was naturally shocked. "I didn't hear you," he added gently.

He heard me, I knew. He just had not expected this request. Joseph was rendering himself unclean by dealing with a dead body. He would be unable to celebrate the Passover because of his kindness to Jesus and to me. He could understand if I wanted to help prepare the body for burial. But wanting to hold him? For my part, I didn't care what he understood. I just didn't care. My son was dead. He would never hug me again—or smile at me again—or reassure me again—I just wanted to hold him one last time. I didn't care what shape his body was in or what anyone thought.

"I want to hold him. Have him brought to me."

Joseph looked down at me helplessly. I said nothing more, just returned his gaze. Finally, he sighed and turned toward his men, motioning them to bring the body near. "Put him on his mother's lap," he said when the men had come close. They hesitated, their eyes filled with questions.

"Do as you are told," Joseph snapped, and Jesus' body was lowered gently into my waiting arms.

I sat very still, the weight of his body heavy on my lap and in my arms, the warmth of life, so recently ended, still in him. I looked at him. He was so battered and beaten, there was hardly anything left of the Jesus I knew and loved. Yet there he was. I thanked God that I had not known when he was a baby that this was his destination. I remembered the day of his dedication at the temple. "Oh, my poor dear Simeon," I whispered. "You knew…"

After a bit, I looked up to find that another man had joined Joseph. I recognized him. It was Nicodemus, the Pharisee. It had been rumored that he admired Jesus, but if anyone asked, he would say, "No." Was he here to cause trouble? It didn't matter now. But, no, he and Joseph seemed on good terms. They started in my direction. John was still beside me.

"Are you ready, Mother?" Joseph asked. I had had little rest since I left Nazareth on Tuesday, other than the night's sleep at the home of Mary and Martha. Today had begun so early and had been so draining. I nodded weakly. I was ready.

Nicodemus and Joseph lifted Jesus' body from my lap and started toward the tomb. John reached down and helped me to my feet. We followed the men and the body closely until we reached a bench a short distance from the burial chamber. Here was a place provided for people who would come to be near the dead, but not so near as to be defiled. I sat down. John stayed near me, and we watched as the two men washed Jesus' body in the proper way, cleaning away the blood and dirt of abuse. Next they rubbed his body with olive oil mixed with perfume to cover the stench of death. Then Jesus was wrapped carefully in strips of cloth. Hesitating, the men looked sadly one last time upon the face of the one they loved. Finally, covering that face with a linen napkin, they bound his head.

When all was ready, Nicodemus and Joseph lifted the body and passed it through the small rectangular opening into the dark chamber of the tomb. There Jesus was laid on a stone bench that had been carved out of the rock. John and I looked in. A lamp burned in a small niche in the wall above the body, shining its light into the darkness of the tomb, just as my son's life had shone light into the darkness of the world.

I remembered the manger. Here was my son, once again wrapped in strips of cloth and laid on cold stone, just as he had been at his birth.

Determined that Jesus should have the burial of a king, Joseph spared no expense. He had bought seventy-five pounds of spices, which he now packed into the tomb in order to prevent any smell from escaping. The rock was placed before the entrance. The burial was complete. The Sabbath began. It was the day upon which our God had rested after the creation at the beginning of time. Now the Son of God rested after the new creation at the beginning of a new time.

CHAPTER 18

He's Alive!

I had it in mind that I would go back to the home of Mary and Martha when everything was over, but when Jesus commended me to John, my situation changed. With the burial complete, John took me to the guest room where he and Jesus and the others had eaten the evening before. It was a welcome change of plans since the room was in Jerusalem and much closer than Bethany. I was so physically tired and emotionally drained that all I wanted to do was rest.

When we reached the room where we would spend the next couple of days, a few of the disciples were already there. The others straggled in one by one—except for Judas, whom I never saw again. But those who came!—such a bedraggled, exhausted, depressed, guilt-ridden, hopeless looking crew could not be imagined, and I think my presence was a bit of a thorn in their flesh—a live reminder of their teacher—a presence that kept them from saying what they wanted to say. They were uncomfortably quiet, so I finally decided I would break the silence.

"I didn't think it would end this way," I said, and I paused. Two or three seconds of silence followed. Then mouths opened, and the disciples slowly began to pour out their thoughts and feelings. The fishermen in the group told how they had left their businesses in the hands of others in order to follow Jesus, and how they never were comfortable with having someone else in charge. Their families had been left behind. It had been a real hardship being apart—the loneliness, the moments unshared that could never be recaptured. But they had thought it would be worth it—until now. Then Matthew spoke of how he had given up his means of livelihood and had nothing to go back to. Whereas before, only Jews had hated Matthew, now Roman and Jew alike held him in contempt. Another began to blame Judas that things had ended this way, and very quickly his name became the target of all the anger the group was feeling.

They had given up everything, and for what?! Now their leader was dead; their lives were in danger. They poured out their souls, and when they had no more to say, they sat staring at the floor. In the silence my heart ached for them, but even in the face of what I had seen, I could not completely share their despair. He had said he would live again! "Trust me!" his strong voice echoed in my memory.

Finally one of them looked at me. "Sorry, Mother of Jesus. We're not saying that it wasn't worth it. Over the last three years we've seen things that no one will ever believe. I know I'm a better person for it all. I'll never be the same. It's just that… well, like you said, we didn't think it would end this way either."

"But it hasn't ended," I said. "Don't you see what he's started? His life changed you. And because of that, your lives will change others. As long as the effect he had on you continues, he lives on.

"Besides," I added, dropping my voice, talking more to myself than to the men, "he said he'd die and rise from death. He brought back Lazarus. He asked me to trust him even when things didn't make sense. I'm going to try."

Some of the men seemed not to hear me at all. Others, looked me as though I were a crazy old woman who had to be humored, and, saying nothing, returned to their own thoughts. I dropped my head and stared at the floor, lost in doubts that I would not admit to these men. Perhaps I believed only because believing relieved the pain of knowing that my son was dead. I knew that whenever I tried to accept the fact that he really was dead, that his life was over, the grief weighed so heavily that I searched for a way out. I had to believe in order to survive! Was it just a survival technique then? No, there was more to it than that. It was a feeling I had—but more than a feeling. If Jesus really meant exactly what he said, the best was yet to come. However, these men did not seem open to such thoughts, so I resigned myself to silence.

As I sat struggling between my own need to believe and my penchant for facing reality, I heard Peter suggest to one of the others that they go to a nearby Roman establishment for some wine. Poor Peter. Having denied Jesus, only to learn later that Jesus was dead, was too much. Peter had put his life on the line in the garden, but Jesus had stopped him.[1] Now Jesus was dead, and Peter's despair was so complete that he felt desperate

1. John 18:10

for a way out. Another disciple, I don't remember which one it was—Andrew, perhaps—said, "I think it would be better if we stayed here. We could end up like Jesus, and what would that accomplish?" He spoke slowly and quietly, almost in a monotone, seeming to make the statement more to himself than to others. His head dropped so that he seemed to stare almost at his own waist. Then lifting his face momentarily he said, "There's Passover wine here if anyone feels a need for it." Shifting his lifeless, weary eyes to Peter, he continued in the same quiet voice, without agitation, but very directly, "Forget what you did. We all betrayed him in our own way[2]—except maybe John." He paused, holding Peter in his gaze. "Stop thinking that you should be held to higher standards than the rest of us. Jesus loved you! But not because you were perfect!" And he slowly lowered his face again.

"Some Passover!" someone muttered.

By this time fatigue had crept over me, and I had begun to feel like Andrew looked. All the hours without sleep, at the end of a quick trip down from the Galilee, were having an effect on me. My head began to nod, and John rolled out a mat for me and gave me a cushion for my head. I lay down vaguely aware that I had not eaten for twenty-four hours, but I was more in need of sleep than food or drink.

It was a restless night. Throughout the dark hours, many times, I roused enough to be aware of movement around me—men getting food or something to drink, or just moving around, unable to sleep and needing to stretch. Occasionally one wept, another snored.

With dawn came a new day, although it was not a day that was greeted with enthusiasm. The rising sun normally stood as a reminder that God was in his heaven and still in control, but at this dawn we had significant doubts. The fatigue, the grief, the shock of all that had happened, the despair that enveloped us all, took its toll, capturing my memory and keeping me from remembering, even to this day, most of that time span. Some of the men must have gone out for a while, because we got news of Judas' death. But mostly I think the day was spent there, in the room.

Judas' death was a shock, and the effect that it had on the others was not good. It seemed to solidify their anger and contempt toward him, and that continued throughout their lives, filtering into the writing that

2. In Matthew 26:21 all indicate thoughts of betrayal. John alone was at the cross.

bears their names. Looking back, though, I think Judas had to do what he did, because Jesus had to die. I don't believe that Judas ever thought his betrayal would lead to Jesus' death. Jesus trusted Judas—had him keep the money for the group. And Jesus loved Judas. His last action toward Judas had been one of love.[3] Then he had told Judas to go and do what he had to do.[4] I think maybe Judas believed—trusted—Jesus more than any of the others, and so he tried to force Jesus to make his move and establish his throne. It was just that, like the others, he did not understand how Jesus was going to be enthroned, or exactly what the nature of his kingdom was to be. And when Judas realized what had happened, he just could not live with it. Peter claimed later that while Jesus was dead, he descended into hell to visit the lost souls. I think he must have found Judas there, and I think they must have embraced—two old friends, one with nail holes in his hands and feet, a spear wound in his side, and the other with rope burns on his neck. I'm sure Jesus forgave him. I wish the other disciples could have.

At any rate, the day passed, ending at six o'clock Saturday evening. The Sabbath was over and the first day of the new week had begun. It was like the first of all first days at the beginning of time. It was the beginning of a new creation, a new world, new life for all who would have it, although we did not know that at the time.

It was very early on that first day when Mary Magdalene came running into the darkness of our lives bringing the first glimpse of light. Breathless, she burst into the room and into that cloud of gloom that hung so heavily over us. Startled, we stared at her silently as she managed a few desperate words between her equally desperate gasps for breath; "Peter... John... He's gone... They've taken his body... and I don't know where... they've laid him." Peter and John were up and running from the room before anyone else even grasped what had been said. They had been explosively tense all day, and Mary Magdalene's words triggered them. And poor Mary, must have gotten her second wind, because she took off running after them, still so breathless she could barely breathe an "Ohhh..."

Shocked, the rest of us just looked at the open door for awhile. Then someone said, "Did she say his body was missing?"

---

3. Jesus fed Judas, which in that culture is an intimate way of saying, "I love you."
4. John 13:26

"That's what it sounded like," another answered.

I sighed and stepped outside the door to a portion of the roof of the house that was left as a balcony for those who used the guest room. Near the top of the steps that led to the street below, I stopped to feel the fresh air and to think. We had buried Jesus so carefully, and now the body was gone. Still… there was that glimmering flame of hope within that refused to die.

I had not been standing long, staring into that desert sky, when I heard the sound of men talking in the streets. A feeling of fear gripped me momentarily, and then I saw Peter and John. They started up the stairs, and then, looking up, saw me standing there. "I'm sorry, Mary," said John as he came near. "He's gone."

"They took off the burial cloths," said Peter, his temper showing. "Can you believe it? They unwrapped his body!"

"Peter!" John exclaimed. "We were going to spare her!"

"I'm sorry," said Peter. "I just can't believe it! Why, by now his body would be bloated and…"

"Peter!" John looked at Peter sternly.

Peter went silently past me and into the room. I knew what he was going to say. The body would now be decayed, smelling and seeping, eyes bulging out. I looked at John. "They unwrapped him?" It was unthinkable!

He nodded and was silent for a bit, as though struggling with whether or not to tell me something. Then, seeing my questioning eyes, he spoke.

"It's curious, Mother! The cloths were all just lying there except for the head cloth! You know, the one we used to pull his chin up and tied over the top of his head to keep his mouth shut? It was rolled up and lying at the end of the shelf under the niche where the lamp burns." He looked at me for a moment and then went on. "It's almost as though he's telling us that he can't be silenced. He was God's Word to us and that Word will continue to speak and bring light into the world. I know he's dead, and yet…" John stopped and looked far off. "Is it God's way of saying that, although he's dead, he will not be silenced? Or…" John couldn't bring himself to go on. And I could understand. My own throat thickened and ached, and I was near tears. I wanted to believe that Jesus lived, and it would be so like him to leave the head cloth rolled up that way, and chuckle as he thought of it being found by those who loved him. But he had been killed! I had helped bury him! Did I dare to hope? Or would I just be setting myself up to be hurt again? If Jesus' life were over, I wanted to believe it was over—finished! But what if it weren't over, and I gave up? We stood there together, John and I. He slipped his strong arm around my shoulders and gave me a squeeze. "Let's go inside," he said. "I want to get ready to head home to Galilee, if you think you're up to the trip."

As we turned to go inside, we heard someone in the street coming our way. Looking back, we saw that it was Mary Magdalene again! I suddenly realized with remorse that I had given no further thought to her once she had taken off—her breath already spent—running after the men. Now she waved her arms as she half fell, half ran toward us. She seemed to have more news. Could it be she had found the body? I doubted she would know for sure if she had. The body would hardly be recognizable by now.

She slowed as she came up the stairs, again gasping for breath. "I saw... him! I... saw him!" she gasped.

Releasing me, John put his hands out to Mary and helped her up the stairs, speaking as they moved, "Come in and catch your breath, Mary. Then you can tell us where they put him."

"No..." Mary breathed. "I saw... him!" She struggled to speak.

John was maneuvering Mary through the door, and she was resisting. Then she saw the others inside, and she moved ahead. "He's... alive!" she said. "I've... seen him!" She had not yet caught her breath.

Peter moved over and tried to help John get this woman to sit down. "You need to rest," he said. "It's been a hard couple of days for all of us." Then looking at the others, he explained, "She's been running too much. The shock of seeing the tomb empty—the exhaustion—she needs to rest." The others smiled knowing smiles and nodded their understanding of a woman under too much stress.

Looking back at Mary, Peter tried to soothe and quiet her. "Don't worry, we'll find the body."

By this time, John and Peter between them had seated Mary, and she was growing quite angry with their patronizing care and lack of interest in anything she had to say. Even though women were not considered credible witnesses and could not testify in a court, Jesus had always been willing to listen, and Mary had gotten used to being taken seriously. Looking at the way in which these men received Mary, I wondered whether they had learned anything at all from my son.

At any rate, I wanted to hear what this woman was trying to say, so I stepped in. I knew that for Jesus' sake, these men would respect me, even though I, too, was a woman.

"I want to hear what she has to say," I said sternly, putting as much energy into my voice as I could muster. I looked toward Mary as the men grew quiet. Glancing around the room, a little apprehensive after the sort of greeting she had just received, Mary began to tell her story.

"Peter and John left after they looked in the tomb." She gave them a reproachful look, obviously still angry from being manhandled. "But I stayed. I couldn't just leave like they did. I thought I could at least be near where he was, and I thought, 'Who knows? His spirit might have lingered here even if the body's gone.'" Seeing the surprised look on the faces of some of the disciples, she explained, "You know—the third day it leaves the body, so it could be there even if the body's gone. Anyway, I felt his presence." She raised her eyebrows and nodded at the men, her face wearing a sassy condescending look that was underwritten by their rejection of her witness, along with the grief she was afraid to reveal. I could hardly blame her, but she was not helping her cause any. "So, anyway, I decided I didn't care if I got unclean. You know—half the people see me as unclean anyway, but I'm not, because Jesus took care of that. So, I was going to just sit by the memorial,[5] which would be proper, but after you guys went into the tomb, I thought, 'Why not? If they can be unclean, I can be unclean!' So I went over and laid my hand on the tomb, stooped down, and looked in the door to see the burial cloths you said were there." She looked back at Peter and John. "Only when I looked in, there were two angels sitting on the shelf where the body was supposed to be." She was really trying to rub it in, but Peter would have no part of it.

"Angels?" he said. "Angels?! You want us to believe that you saw angels?!"

Undaunted, in fact, energized by Peter's response, Mary looked at Peter out of the corner of her eye, crossed her legs and tossed her foot. Then she went on, ignoring his accusation. "That's not the best part!" She looked directly at Peter. "The angels asked me why I was crying, and I said because they took my Lord away, and I didn't know where the body was,

---

5. A place with a bench near the tomb where people could come to be near the dead without rendering themselves unclean.

although I was really crying because I was so sad and everything and just frustrated." Her voice had thickened. She dropped her eyes to the floor.

"Just get on with it!" growled Peter. He obviously wasn't going to take anything that she had to say very seriously, and he just wanted her to get finished.

Composing herself and looking at Peter again, Mary continued, "As I was saying, I told the ANGELS why I was crying, and then I turned around, and there he was!" She threw her hands into the air with a flourish as though there were no more to say.

"There who was?" demanded Peter.

"Jesus, of course! If you hadn't been in such an all-fired hurry, you'd have seen him, too!"

Peter's face turned bright red. Mary was having the effect she wanted. There had always been a rivalry between these two; he not completely accepting women, she thriving on pushing his buttons and knowing exactly how to do it.

"Mary," I said. She looked at me. I shook my head. "Not now."

Her boldness turned to sheepishness, and she continued. "Jesus was standing right there when I turned around, but I didn't know it was him. I thought it was the gardener!"

"Probably was," muttered Peter. I tapped him on the shoulder, and he slumped down, pulling inside himself. He and Mary obviously regarded me as a mother figure.

Mary went on, ignoring the interruption. "I thought it was the gardener, so I tried to be really nice, because maybe he could help, and I turned away and I said, 'Sir, if you took his body away, could you tell me where you put it, so I can go and get it?'

"You know. I just loved him so much, I didn't care what sort of shape that body was in by now, I just wanted to take care of it!" There were tears in Mary's eyes, and Peter softened a little.

She went on; "Then he said, 'Mary!', and I knew that voice, and I turned back, and there he stood!

"And I said, 'Teacher!', and I reached out for him.

"And he said, 'No, Mary. Don't hold on to me. I still have to ascend to my Father in heaven.' And we just looked into each other's eyes for a moment, and during that moment I was filled with such joy and peace—and a kind of sadness, too. Because somehow, I knew that even though he is alive, things are never going to be the same. I'm not sure you can understand, but I realized that never again will it be Jesus walking down the road with me at his side heading for new adventures. Now it will be me walking down the road with him here." Mary raised her hands and rested them on her breast over her heart. "He'll be with me—in me-- living here in a way that he can't—until he ascends to our God.

"You see…," Mary struggled to put into words what she was feeling. I looked at her, thinking how far Jesus had brought her. Although she was still a bit unpolished, she was a completely different person than she had been when Jesus had found her. Now, because of the changes Jesus had made, combined with all she'd been through in life, she saw things in a way that none of the rest of us could, and we all waited to see what she was going to say.

She clasped her hands around her knees and stared at the floor. "You see," she repeated, "it's like, now, instead of being in one place, in one time, he will be in all places—even in all of us—all of the time! After he ascends, he will be here more than he ever has been! And not just in our lifetimes, but for all time!" Mary's eyes drifted to places unknown, her face filled with wonder. The room was silent. For that moment, no one doubted her.

Slowly Mary returned to the present, and as she realized that she had been revealing her innermost thoughts, that she had made herself more than a little vulnerable, she quickly sought to resume her tough front—without much success.

"Oh, yeah," she said. "He gave me a message for you guys." She looked around the room doubtfully, and all the men silently looked back. They weren't sure what to make of this woman and the things she had to say. Getting no response, she continued. "He said, 'Tell the brothers that I am ascending to my Father and your Father, my God and your God.'"[6] Again there was silence and Mary looked a little doubtful. Finally she finished, "That's what he said to tell you… ascending to my Father and your Father… my God and your God. That's it. So I came to tell you, because that's what he told me to do." Her eyes dropped to the floor and she waited. A tear slid down her cheek.

In the silence that followed, I quickly became lost in my own thoughts. For a while I had put all my feelings on hold, so I could defend

6. John 20:17

Mary and hear what she had to say. Now I thought of what she had said. I was surprised by her story, and yet not surprised. As I continued thinking, my feelings soared from the darkness of doubts brought on by my own reluctance to trust this woman, to an uncontrollable joy that sought to swell my very being when I believed her, only to drop down to the darkness once again, as I feared to hope. On the one hand, she had described what I had thought would happen. On the other hand, how could it be true?

As I thought, I believed more and more, but I was vaguely aware, from the conversations going on around me, that the thoughts of others were moving in a direction opposite to mine. The men had been moved by Mary Magdalene's tale, but they were not able to believe it.

The day passed quickly, it seemed. Once again, I remember little of what happened, aside from Mary's coming. The men stayed inside all day, again frightened that the Judeans might arrest them. In fact, they became so paranoid that they closed the door and locked it.

It was while we were all sitting there in that locked room that Jesus came. It happened suddenly. One minute we were all alone, and the next minute, there he stood.

"Peace be with you!" he said. And it was with us! After so much despair, we had peace! It was the same peace I had known as I trudged back home from Elizabeth's house that day so long ago, a pregnant teen on the way to face her family, her betrothed, and possible stoning. This peace we knew at Jesus' bidding was the same peace I'd seen on the old shepherd's face as he'd held my baby that day so long ago, before returning to his life as an outcast. It was the peace I'd known, staying home while gossiping tongues wagged around me, and Jesus went about his ministry, risking his life. It was the peace that had clung to me and refused to completely let me go even as I had watched my son die a horrible death. It was the peace of continuing hope; hope that refused to disappear, even after I'd buried my son. That peace, that had become so familiar and yet so elusive at times, was now complete. I relaxed and watched my son. He gave me a brief welcome hug, and then turned his attention to the others. I was fulfilled, my life complete. But it was not so with the others. Jesus must convince these hard-headed followers, whom he was trusting to carry on his work, that it was indeed he who was alive. I watched as he showed them the wounds in his side and hands. I saw him breathe on them and give them the Holy Spirit.[7] I saw the disciples rejoice as they finally believed, and I saw Mary Magdalene's triumphant radiant face.

I saw much, and it was simply as an observer that I participated in the next forty days. During that time, Jesus continued to reassure and strengthen these who would soon begin to tell others of him in spite of the danger to themselves. My job was finished. Jesus had placed me in John's tender care, and there I would remain.

It was a busy forty days. I accompanied John and the others up to Galilee and then back to Jerusalem during that time. The men did what they needed to do, and I cooked and mended, encouraged and cautioned, enjoying the company of all these men and women who were friends of my son.

Then one day the men came in and said that Jesus was gone. He had told them goodbye, given them their instructions, and then, before their very eyes, had simply raised up in the air and kept going until he was out of sight. We stayed in Jerusalem after that, and I was with the disciples the day the Holy Spirit filled them with other languages, and people from all over the world heard about my son in words they could understand. And many of them believed the words they heard and became followers! It was an amazing thing! So many amazing things I saw that day and in the days, weeks, and years to come. I was there in Jerusalem to see the church take root and expand. I was in Ephesus with John to see the church there grow under his steady hand and unwavering love. The fellowship that was shared in those days, the love that was shown, the hands that began to reach out to others, the expanse of the effect of my son's life—all these things were amazing to me. But nothing was ever so amazing as the fact that I had been the mother of this Messiah, who had come to bring the peace of the presence of God into the lives of all who would have it. I had simply agreed to be God's slave, and through my submission had come the One through whom all this had occurred. Now I watched, remembered, helped out where I could, and shared the story of my life with any who wanted to hear. And so I lived out my days in God's peace.

May you know His peace in your life.
Amen!

7. John 20:22